16.98

C000263915

Using Humour in
the English Classroom

live
LANGUAGE
live-language.com

Geoff Tranter

Using Humour in the English Classroom

Teaching ideas and activities

Ernst Klett Sprachen
Stuttgart

1st edition   1 $^{5\,4\,3}$ | 2015 14 13 12

The last figure shown denotes the year of impression.

© Ernst Klett Sprachen GmbH, Rotebühlstraße 77, 70178 Stuttgart, 2011.
All rights reserved.
www.klett.de / www.lektueren.com

Editor: Wolfgang Volz
Cover and layout: Elmar Feuerbach
Illustrations: Oliver Lucht, Pfeffer und Salz, Feiburg
Typesetting: Eva Mokhlis, Swabianmedia, Stuttgart
Cover picture: Getty Images (Stone/Gandee Vasan), Munich
Printing and binding: AZ Druck und Datentechnik GmbH, Heisinger Straße 16,
87437 Kempten/Allgäu

Printed in Germany

ISBN 978-3-12-534645-1

Contents

Introduction

This book consists of a number of activity sheets or copymasters that can be photocopied for use in class. They are based on a variety of aspects of English language humour and provide an opportunity for a more light-hearted approach to learning in the classroom. But equally they all have some pedagogical features that will help to support language learning. Depending on the actual activity sheet, they may promote vocabulary learning or there may be a structural background allowing the practice of grammatical items in a more humorous context. They can help to promote language awareness and intercultural awareness (showing how native speakers are able to use language in a humorous way). In addition, the more positive approach that humour can help to create in the classroom should motivate learners to read the texts in more detail and promote reading skills. Playing with the language can also increase people's learning skills, and not least some activities look at stylistic aspects giving the learners an opportunity to compare different styles.

The basic aim of the book is three-fold: to promote

i) understanding, i.e. to understand what is being said on a cognitive level;

ii) appreciation, i.e. the emotional level of understanding and being able to laugh along with native speakers, and

iii) creativity, i.e. the ability to use the various features of English-language humour to create one's own examples.

Basic Procedures for Working with the Copymasters

The majority of the tasks have one of the following formats:

a) Matching, e.g. sentence with sentence, phrase with phrase, question with answer, phrase with picture

b) Speculating, e.g. guessing the meaning, guessing the correct word, guessing the problem / cause / place

c) Writing tasks, e.g. writing sentences to express a certain meaning, writing a letter / article or re-phrasing sentences

d) Sentence completion

e) Unjumbling tasks, e.g. sentences

f) Gap-filling, with or without the first letter(s) of the missing words

g) Creative tasks, e.g. suggest an appropriate name, word, etc.

h) Correction tasks, e.g. correct mistakes

i) Explanation tasks, e.g. explain why something is wrong, amusing, etc.

j) Underlining tasks, e.g. underlining ambiguous words/phrases, wrong words, hidden words, etc.

k) Interpreting tasks, e.g. what did the speaker/writer actually want to express?

l) Discussion tasks, e.g. which do you like best, which is the funniest, etc.

m) Acting tasks, e.g. telling jokes, reading out tongue-twisters, limericks, etc.

With all these formats, the following basic methodology is recommended for the tasks:

1. Do at least one example together with the whole class. If necessary, try a second example. Always make sure that the learners are clear about how to proceed.

2. Divide the class into small working groups. There are many ways of doing this. The best recommendation is to use a procedure that you have used in class before. In matching tasks that consist of two parts, one practical idea is to give each learner one of the items and ask them to find the person with the other half.

3. Let the small groups work on the remaining examples. There are a number of different options: all groups can be asked to do all the examples OR the examples can be shared out, each group doing two or three each. Allow sufficient time accordingly. The use of dictionaries should be allowed if appropriate. Monitor the group work to make sure that the learners are making progress. Help out as and when necessary by giving suitable prompts. Finish the group work when the groups have completed the task.

4. Ask each group to report on the individual examples. If they have been working on the same examples in parallel, go through the whole task example by example. Where appropriate, ask the groups to explain the reasons for their solutions.

Definitions

Droodles

Droodles are visual guessing games where the aim is to work out what the person who devised the droodle is trying to express. They can be based on drawings (non-verbal) or on letters and words (verbal droodles). They are sometimes known as pictograms or rebuses although these names normally refer to the non-verbal category.

The name droodle (the word comes from "doodle" = idle drawing and "riddle" = a quiz item) was used by the American Roger Price in his book "Doodles" in 1953. The format is often found in newspapers, and there even was a TV game show based on the same concept in America.

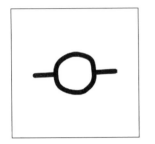

Introduction: Show the four droodles on the left as an introduction to the principle of droodles (best draw them on the board): There are a number of different categories, e.g. things seen from a different angle = a) a Mexican on a bicycle, and b) a bear climbing a tree, OR a small cut-out from a larger object = c) a man with a bow tie caught in a lift, and d) a chessboard for beginners – alternatively for non-intellectuals a draughts board for beginners.

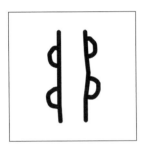

Task 1: Guessing: Ask the class to guess the meaning of the first three examples. After each example, point out the principles behind these examples, e.g.: position, sounds, size, direction, numbers. As a follow-up, divide the class into groups and ask each group to make similar examples to present to the class. If appropriate, words and phrases from the course book or those dealt with in one of the last lessons can be given as a basis for the task.

Task 2: Guessing: Ask the class to work in the same or different groups and guess the meaning of as many of the examples as they can. They can also be asked to explain the principles (cf. above).

Task 3: Creating own examples: Divide the class into groups and ask each group to choose 2-3 of the words and phrases and make droodles to be presented to the whole class. Finally any words or phrases that are left over can be solved by the whole class in plenary.

Acronyms

Acronyms are words formed from the initial letters or parts of a phrase or a name, e.g. RADAR, NATO, FAQ or AIDS. There are thousands, perhaps even millions of acronyms – the ones used for this activity page were chosen for their humorous character.

Acronyms can be used for promoting creative use of language in the classroom, but are also useful for lexical work, especially with the examples on this activity sheet.

The droodle format can be used quite effectively in the classroom as a motivating vocabulary learning technique.

All three tasks are basically of the same format – each task based on a different topic area 1) airlines; 2) cars; 3) social groups. The three tasks need not be used altogether in one classroom session. They can be used on separate occasions, ideally when one particular topic is being dealt with in the course book, as this might prove helpful in finding suitable words.

To make the task a little easier to do, some of the words have been provided in full; in other cases the first letter has been given. With a very creative group it might be possible to simply give the group the acronyms, either straight away or after one or two attempts. In this case, it is only necessary to write the acronyms on the board.

Refer to Page 6 for basic ways of dealing with these tasks.

Additional tips are:

• Ask the class what words the letters might stand for, e.g. What words do you know in connection with air travel? What might "J" stand for?

• There is of course more than one solution to these activities. Providing the sentence or phrase produced makes sense and is linguistically possible, all alternatives to the Key can be accepted.

• The final task is an open-ended activity that can and should be used at the end of term. Anything is possible!

Funny Definitions

The definitions used as the basis for this and the following copymaster are humorous, often satirical reinterpretations of everyday words and phrases, the normal meanings of which can be found in any standard dictionary. A good source of such definitions over and beyond the examples used here is "The Devil's Dictionary" written by Ambrose Bierce at the beginning of the 20th century. The Devil's Dictionary is available on the internet from where you can print out a number of pages.

The exercises aim to focus on vocabulary and also practise the skill of Reading for Detail. On Copymaster I there are two matching activities followed by a guessing task, the tasks on Copymaster II are guessing activities in specific topic areas.

• The tasks should be used in the sequence they are presented, as they proceed from the receptive approach of matching to the productive approach of finding the correct word.

• In the guessing tasks, use if necessary prompts like "What kind of foreigners do you find here in …?", "Where would you go?", "What buildings do travellers pass through?", "When do people eat and drink?" or "What does the number 365 refer to?", etc.

• As a follow-up, there is the possibility of having a short discussion by asking questions like: "Do you agree with the definition?" "Do you think the definition is humorous?" "Why?"

After working through the copymasters, and if the class is interested in this kind of language work, you could give each group a couple of pages from The Devil's Dictionary, each with different definitions, and the groups can choose words for other groups to define and/or definitions for the other groups to solve.

Proverbs

According to Wikipedia, a proverb is a simple and concrete saying popularly known and repeated, which expresses a truth, based on common sense or the practical experience of humanity, e.g. "A stitch in time saves nine". The three copymasters provide examples of traditional English proverbs, modern proverbs and international proverbs translated into English.

This section combines many aspects of language: e.g. the intercultural aspect of proverbs, creative use of language, word order.

Copymaster I provides in Task 1 a sentence completion exercise. Allow the use of dictionaries. As a follow-up, the meaning can be discussed and the class can be asked for similar proverbs in their own language, especially in groups with different nationalities. Task 2 is a matching exercise. The alternative endings in this Task were suggested by schoolchildren in a competition. Task 3 provides more traditional English proverbs for completion, after which the class can make alternative humorous suggestions to complete the proverb. If necessary, use question prompts (e.g. 1. "Who takes away people's money?").

Copymaster II is an unjumbling exercise. Help the class with prompts, e.g. "What kind of word follows the opening words?", and tell them to look out for the punctuation marks mid-sentence.

Copymaster III has international proverbs which have been translated into English. Task 1 is a matching exercise; the task can be left to groups to work out themselves. Task 2 is a gap-filling exercise. If necessary, offer a few question prompts to guide the learners in the right direction. As a follow-up, ask the class what they think the proverbs mean, and/or whether there is a similar proverb in their language and which of the international proverbs they like best.

PC Language

Political correctness (PC) is avoiding language, actions, ideas or policies which could be offensive to other people in terms of occupations, gender, race, culture, age, religious beliefs, sexual orientation or disability. For example: *steward/ stewardess* is not considered PC; the gender-neutral word is *flight attendant*. Similarly the word *Indian*. The politically correct expression is *Native American* in US or *First Nation* in Canada. And the word *blind* becomes *visually challenged*. Many of such words are now commonly used, others less so.

The first copymaster covers the various types of phrases that can be formed. The purpose of these tasks is not so much to encourage active use, which can be a little risky in certain contexts, but to enhance receptive understanding of these phrases when seen or heard, and in this way to increase language awareness.

Copymaster I: Tasks 1 and 2 are both matching exercises to demonstrate the range of language involved. In Task 1 it should be explained that all six alternatives in the second column can be combined with all the adverbs. Task 3 is a guessing activity.

Copymaster II: The examples in Task 1 are not authentic examples of PC language. The strategies used in the PC examples on Copymaster I have been adapted to produce examples from within the context of English language, the aim being to demonstrate how the PC strategies can be used in other contexts for fun purposes. Task 2 is an underlining activity based on a well-known fairy tale that has been put into PC language.

Murphy's Law

Murphy's Law is what people talk about when things have gone wrong. The Law basically says:

"If anything can go wrong, it will!"

Although this principle has been known since the 19th century it was only known as Murphy's Law from about 1950 onwards. Information on who exactly Murphy was seems to have disappeared in the course of time. There are many variations on Murphy's Law and these are the basis for the tasks on this activity sheet.

The activities are quite useful for higher-level classes, in particular classes that are concerned with language in professional contexts, e.g. Business or Technical English, firstly because the vocabulary is workplace-oriented and secondly because both Tasks 1 and 2 use typical structures found in such contexts. They can however also be used effectively in general courses with learners who have some general knowledge of how things work.

Task 1 is a matching activity to be done in small groups. Task 2 is a fill-in exercise.

Oxymorons

An oxymoron is a literary device consisting of words that contradict each other. Sometimes this type of contradictory phrase is used deliberately to create a certain effect, e.g. "deafening silence", or "a serious joke". Often they are the result of mistakes during spontaneous speech, e.g. "a definite possibility" .

The activities on this copymaster require learners to think about words and the meanings of words and to increase their language awareness. They can also be used as a springboard for a discussion on the way politicians and journalists use language to influence people's views and emotions, e.g. "friendly fire".

Task 1 and Task 2 are matching exercises. An alternative would be to give each learner in the class one half of the oxymoron on cards and ask them to find the other half. Having done so they should present the oxymoron to the rest of the class and explain the contradiction and the possible humorous effect.

Task 3 is purely for discussion purposes. The groups work on one or two each, and then present their opinions on those particular examples.

Droodles

Task 1) *What do the following droodles mean? Write your answers in the spaces provided.*

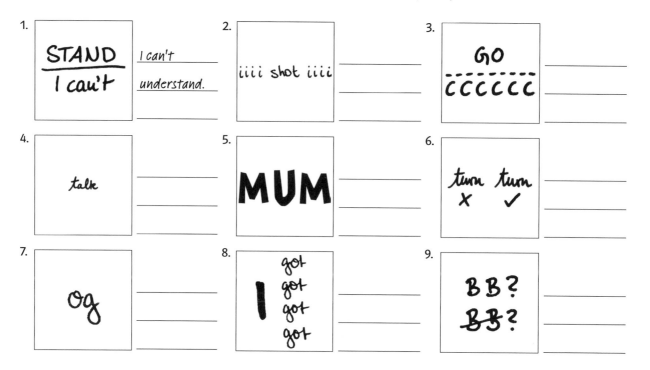

1. STAND / I can't — *I can't understand.*

2. iiii shot iiii — _____

3. GO / CCCCCC — _____

4. talk — _____

5. **MUM** — _____

6. turn turn / x ✓ — _____

7. Og — _____

8. I got got got got — _____

9. BB? / B̶B̶? — _____

Task 2) *Get together in groups and work out what the following droodles mean.*

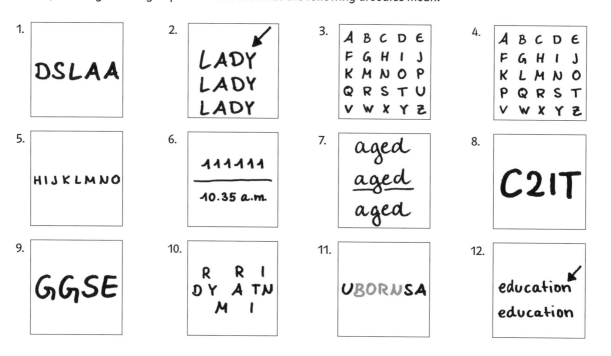

1. DSLAA

2. LADY LADY LADY ↖

3.
A B C D E
F G H I J
K M N O P
Q R S T U
V W X Y Z

4.
A B C D E
F G H I J
K L M N O
P Q R S T
V W X Y Z

5. HIJKLMNO

6. 111111 / 10.35 a.m.

7. aged aged aged

8. C2IT

9. GGSE

10. R R I / D Y A T N / M I

11. UBORNSA

12. education education ↙

Task 3) *Now create your own droodles from the following words.*

1. Mother-in-law
2. Just in case
3. Quite right
4. Back door
5. Afternoon tea
6. Three blind mice
7. Crossroads
8. Mixed pickles
9. Tuesday
10. Two degrees below zero

© Ernst Klett Sprachen GmbH, Stuttgart 2011
Photocopiable
ISBN 978-3-12-534645-1

Klett

Acronyms

Task 1) *Make humorous phrases or sentences from the following airline acronyms.*

1. AIR INDIA **A**fter **I** r*eturn*_____ **I**'ll n*ever*_____ **d**o it a*gain*_____.
2. ALITALIA **A**lways **I**_____ **i**n **t**_____ **a**lways **I**_____ **i**n **a**_____.
3. DELTA **D**on't **e**_____ **l**uggage **t**_____ **a**rrive.
4. EL AL **E**very **I**_____ **a**lways **I**_____.
5. KLM **K**eeps **I**_____ **m**_____.
6. LOT **L**ots **o**_____ **t**_____!
7. PIA **P**rayers **i**_____ (the) **a**_____!
8. SABENA **S**_____ **a** **b**_____ **e**xperience − **n**_____ **a**gain!
9. TAP **T**_____ **a**nother **p**_____.
10. TWA **T**he **w**_____ **a**_____.

Task 2) *Make humorous phrases or sentences from the following car acronyms.*

1. BMW **B**ig **m**_____ **w**_____.
2. FIAT **F**unny **I**_____ **a**ttempt (at) **t**_____.
3. FORD **F**ix **o**_____ **r**_____ **d**aily.
4. HONDA **H**ad **o**_____ **n**ever **d**_____ **a**_____.
5. JEEP **J**ust **e**_____ **e**ssential **p**_____.
6. PORSCHE **P**roof of **r**_____ **s**poiled **c**_____ **h**aving **e**_____.
7. TOYOTA **T**he **o**_____ **y**ou **o**_____ **t**o **a**_____.
8. VW **V**_____ **w**orthless.

Task 3) *The following acronyms stand for social groups. Fill in the gaps.*

1. DINKY **D**_____ **i**ncome **n**_____ **k**ids **y**_____.
2. HEW **H**_____ **e**_____ **w**orker.
3. HOPEFUL **H**ard-up **o**_____ **p**erson **e**_____ **f**_____ **u**seful **l**_____.
4. MUPPIE **M**_____ **u**_____ **p**rofessional.
5. NEET **N**_____ (in) **e**_____, **e**ducation (or) **t**_____.
6. SADFAB **S**ingle **a**_____ **d**esperate **f**_____ **a** **b**_____.
7. SINBAD **S**ingle **i**_____ **n**o **b**_____ **a**_____ **d**_____.
8. WOOP **W**_____ -**o**_____ **o**lder **p**_____.

Task 4) *Try to make phrases or sentences from the name of your country, your town, a friend of yours, your teacher, etc.*

ALEC **A**lways **l**ate **e**ver **c**harming

DORTMUND **D**ortmund **o**ffers **r**eally **t**hirsty **m**en **u**nlimited **n**utritious **d**rinking

 © Ernst Klett Sprachen GmbH, Stuttgart 2011
Photocopiable
ISBN 978-3-12-534645-1

Funny Definitions I

Task 1) *Find the correct definition for for each of the following people.*

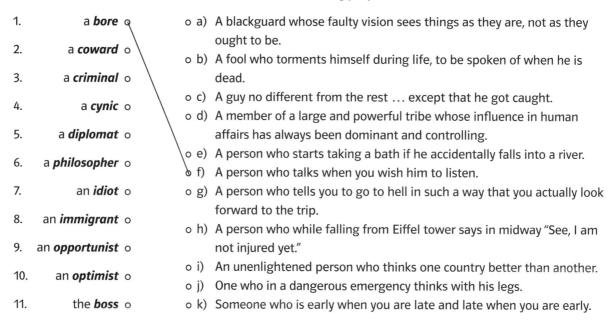

1.	a **bore** ○	○ a)	A blackguard whose faulty vision sees things as they are, not as they ought to be.
2.	a **coward** ○	○ b)	A fool who torments himself during life, to be spoken of when he is dead.
3.	a **criminal** ○	○ c)	A guy no different from the rest … except that he got caught.
4.	a **cynic** ○	○ d)	A member of a large and powerful tribe whose influence in human affairs has always been dominant and controlling.
5.	a **diplomat** ○	○ e)	A person who starts taking a bath if he accidentally falls into a river.
6.	a **philosopher** ○	○ f)	A person who talks when you wish him to listen.
7.	an **idiot** ○	○ g)	A person who tells you to go to hell in such a way that you actually look forward to the trip.
8.	an **immigrant** ○	○ h)	A person who while falling from Eiffel tower says in midway "See, I am not injured yet."
9.	an **opportunist** ○	○ i)	An unenlightened person who thinks one country better than another.
10.	an **optimist** ○	○ j)	One who in a dangerous emergency thinks with his legs.
11.	the **boss** ○	○ k)	Someone who is early when you are late and late when you are early.

Task 2) *Choose the correct answer for the definitions 1.–12.*

1. An agreeable sensation arising from contemplating the misery of another. ○
2. An ingenious instrument which indicates what kind of weather we are having. ○
3. An instrument used chiefly for putting dead animals into one's mouth. ○
4. An invention to end all inventions. ○
5. In that stage of usefulness which is not inconsistent with general inefficiency. ○
6. Once too often. ○
7. The art of dividing a cake so that everybody believes he got the biggest piece. ○
8. The finger commonly used in pointing out two malefactors. ○
9. The most acceptable form of hypocrisy. ○
10. The virtue which induces us to feed and lodge certain persons who are not in need of food and lodging. ○
11. To create a vacancy without nominating a successor. ○
12. To lay the foundation for a future offence. ○

- ○ a) to **apologize**
- ○ b) **atom bomb**
- ○ c) **barometer**
- ○ d) **compromise**
- ○ e) **forefinger**
- ○ f) **fork**
- ○ g) **happiness**
- ○ h) **hospitality**
- ○ i) to **kill**
- ○ j) **old**
- ○ k) **politeness**
- ○ l) **twice**

Task 3) *What do the following definitions refer to?*

1. *a tourist*   A foreigner who is not where he belongs.
2. _____ A place where you can always get a drink when the pubs are closed.
3. _____ A shopping centre travellers have to pass through.
4. _____ The time of year devoted to eat, drinking and overspending.
5. _____ A series of 365 disappointments.

© Ernst Klett Sprachen GmbH, Stuttgart 2011
Photocopiable
ISBN 978-3-12-534645-1

Klett

Funny Definitions II

Task 1) *The following definitions are connected with family and personal relationships. Can you guess what they are?*

1. A personal banker provided by nature – *father*

2. People that you visit or visit you according to whether they are rich or poor – _____

3. A woman with a fine prospect of happiness behind her – _____

4. Future tense of marriage – _____

5. One who, having dined, is charged with the care of the plate – _____

6. The first and worst of all disasters – _____

7. A group of people consisting of a master, a mistress and two slaves, making in all, two – _____

8. A man that is still being sampled by women – _____

9. A group of people that increases in number the more successful you are – _____

Task 2) *The following definitions refer to people and things connected with the state or the country where we live. Can you guess what they are? Write your answers on a separate piece of paper.*

a passport

1. A document treacherously inflicted upon a citizen going abroad, exposing him as an alien.
2. A woman by whom the realm is ruled when there is a king, and through whom it is ruled when there is not.
3. In diplomacy, a last demand before resorting to concessions.
4. In international affairs, a period of cheating between two periods of fighting.
5. In politics, an abrupt change in the form of misgovernment.
6. One who shakes your hand before elections and your confidence afterwards.
7. The instrument and symbol of a man's power to make a fool of himself and a wreck of his country.
8. The patriotic art of lying for one's country.
9. The seat of misgovernment.

Task 3) *The following definitions refer to language and communication between people. Can you guess what they are? Write your answers on a separate piece of paper.*

a gourmet restaurant

1. A place that serves cold soup on purpose.
2. A person that has stopped growing at both ends and is now growing in the middle.
3. A body that keeps minutes and wastes hours.
4. In bad company.
5. One of the greatest labour-saving devices found today.
6. Cutting money in half without damaging the paper.
7. The art of transferring information from the notes of the professor to the notes of the students without passing through the minds of either.
8. The place where success comes before work.
9. A man who looks at all the other people when a beautiful girl enters the room.
10. The only animals you eat before they are born and after they are dead.

© Ernst Klett Sprachen GmbH, Stuttgart 2011
Photocopiable
ISBN 978-3-12-534645-1

Proverbs and Idioms I

Task 1) *Complete the following proverbs. Check in a dictionary.*

1. A bird in the hand is *worth two in the bush.* _____

2. A miss is as good as a _____

3. Better to be safe than _____

4. Children should be seen and not _____

5. Don't bite the hand that _____

6. He who laughs last, _____

7. Laugh and the whole world laughs with you, cry and _____

8. Where there's smoke, there's _____

9. You can't teach an old dog new _____

10. People who live in glass houses should _____

Task 2) *Children were asked to provide alternative endings to the proverbs above. To match their suggestions write the number of the beginnings on the line before the letter.*

_10_ a) … change clothes in basement. ____ e) … pollution.   ____ i) … thinks slowest.
____ b) … looks dirty.   ____ f) … punch a fifth-grader.   ____ j) … you have to blow
____ c) … mathematics.   ____ g) … safer than one overhead.   your nose.
____ d) … Mr.   ____ h) … spanked.

Task 3) *Finish the following proverbs, first in the original version and then in a new, funnier version.*

1. A penny saved *is a penny gained.* _____

2. If at first you don't succeed, _____

3. If something is worth doing, _____

4. Strike while the _____

5. It's better to have loved and lost, _____

6. To err is human, _____

7. Two's company, three's _____

© Ernst Klett Sprachen GmbH, Stuttgart 2011
Photocopiable
ISBN 978-3-12-534645-1

Klett

Proverbs and Idioms II

Task: *Unjumble the words in brackets to discover some modern proverbs.*

1. A clear _conscience is usually the sign of a bad memory._
   (a – bad – conscience – is – memory. – of – sign – the – usually)

2. If you must _____
   (before. – between – choose – evils, – never – one – pick – the – tried – two – you've)

3. It is _____
   (easier – forgiveness – get – permission. – than – to)

4. If you _____
   (like – look – need – passport – picture, – the – trip. – you – your)

5. A conscience _____
   (all – feel – good. – hurts – is – other – parts – what – when – your)

6. No _____
   (been – dishes. – doing – ever – has – husband – shot – the – while)

7. The best way _____
   (a – do – glance. – housework – is – room – sweep – the – the – to – to – with)

8. Always yield _____
   (again. – because – it – may – not – pass – temptation, – to – way – your)

9. There are _____
   (any – cuts – going. – no – place – short – to – worth)

10. You cannot _____
    (bottom. – by – get – on – sitting – the – to – top – your)

11. Going to church _____
    (a – a – any – doesn't – garage – going – holy – make – makes – mechanic. – more – than – to – you – you)

12. A man who _____
    (a – arms – arms – find – her – his – in – into – sink. – sinks – soon – will – woman's)

© Ernst Klett Sprachen GmbH, Stuttgart 2011
Photocopiable
ISBN 978-3-12-534645-1

Proverbs and Idioms III

Task 1) *Choose the correct words from the box to complete the following international proverbs.*

conscience	gets away	host in a year	interest on debts	shepherd
crocodiles	guests	intents	label	too tired

1. *Conscience* is the nest where all good is hatched. *(Welsh Proverb)*

2. _____ grows without rain. *(Yiddish Proverb)*

3. A bicycle can't stand on its own because it's _____. *(English Proverb)*

4. A guest sees more in an hour than the _____. *(Polish Proverb)*

5. A lazy _____ is the wolf's best friend. *(Welsh Proverb)*

6. After three days, both fish and _____ begin to smell. *(Danish Proverb)*

7. Don't rely on the _____ on the bag. *(French Proverb)*

8. Don't think there are no _____ because the water is calm. *(Malaysian Proverb)*

9. Every fish that _____ appears great. *(Turkish Proverb)*

10. Girls who go camping must beware of evil _____. *(Chinese Proverb)*

Task 2) *Complete the following international proverbs.*

1. In a closed mouth, _____ do not enter. *(Mexican Proverb)*

2. It's in old kettles that one makes the best _____. *(French Proverb)*

3. Man who drives like _____ bound to get there. *(Chinese Proverb)*

4. Men who eat many _____ get good run for money. *(Chinese Proverb)*

5. Man with one _____ goes hungry. *(Chinese Proverb)*

6. Money isn't everything, but it sure keeps the kids _____ _____. *(US Proverb)*

7. Money makes _____ of men. *(Icelandic Proverb)*

8. Never let your feet run faster than your _____. *(Scottish Proverb)*

9. The woman who doesn't wish to _____ _____ spends five days sifting the flour. *(Greek Proverb)*

10. There is hope as long as your _____-_____ is in the water. *(Norwegian Proverb)*

© Ernst Klett Sprachen GmbH, Stuttgart 2011
Photocopiable
ISBN 978-3-12-534645-1

Klett

PC Language I

Task 1) *Combine words from the two columns on the left to make a phrase with the same meaning as one of the words and phrases in the right-hand column.*

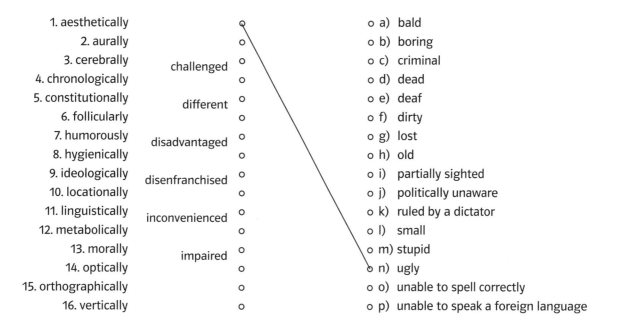

1. aesthetically
2. aurally
3. cerebrally
4. chronologically
5. constitutionally
6. follicularly
7. humorously
8. hygienically
9. ideologically
10. locationally
11. linguistically
12. metabolically
13. morally
14. optically
15. orthographically
16. vertically

challenged
different
disadvantaged
disenfranchised
inconvenienced
impaired

- a) bald
- b) boring
- c) criminal
- d) dead
- e) deaf
- f) dirty
- g) lost
- h) old
- i) partially sighted
- j) politically unaware
- k) ruled by a dictator
- l) small
- m) stupid
- n) ugly
- o) unable to spell correctly
- p) unable to speak a foreign language

Task 2) *Guess the meaning of the following phrases.*

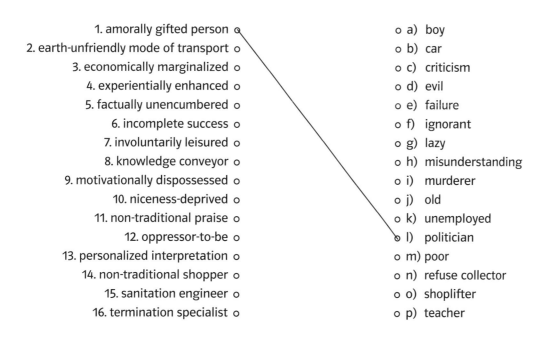

1. amorally gifted person
2. earth-unfriendly mode of transport
3. economically marginalized
4. experientially enhanced
5. factually unencumbered
6. incomplete success
7. involuntarily leisured
8. knowledge conveyor
9. motivationally dispossessed
10. niceness-deprived
11. non-traditional praise
12. oppressor-to-be
13. personalized interpretation
14. non-traditional shopper
15. sanitation engineer
16. termination specialist

- a) boy
- b) car
- c) criticism
- d) evil
- e) failure
- f) ignorant
- g) lazy
- h) misunderstanding
- i) murderer
- j) old
- k) unemployed
- l) politician
- m) poor
- n) refuse collector
- o) shoplifter
- p) teacher

© Ernst Klett Sprachen GmbH, Stuttgart 2011
Photocopiable
ISBN 978-3-12-534645-1

PC Language II

Task 1) *The following examples are taken from language teaching. Guess what they might be.*

1. Arbitrary rules of literacy procedure subservient to a sexist political agenda – *grammar*

2. To be disoriented in terms of needs assessment ethics – _____

3. Lexically different / interesting – _____

4. Member of the question-privileged minority – _____

5. Non-communicatively enhanced language level for the language-skill-disadvantaged – _____

6. Question-deprived person – _____

7. Significant other (language) – _____

8. To be temporarily grammatically and lexically abled – _____

9. To have a deficiency-enhanced result – _____

Task 2) *Read the following PC version of a traditional fairy tale. Mark examples of PC and non-PC language.*

Three Little Pigs

Once upon a time three little pigs co-existed in mutual respect and in harmony with their surroundings. They built beautiful homes from materials that were indigenous to their area. One pig built a house made from straw, one from sticks, and the third pig built a house made from dung, clay, and vines baked in a small oven. After the homes were completed, the pigs were happy with their work and settled back to live in peace and independence.

But one day there came a big, bad wolf with colonialist ideas. Seeing the pigs he became very hungry, both physically and ideologically. The pigs immediately ran into the house made from straw. The wolf ran to the house. Banging on the door he cried, "Little pigs, let me in!" But they shouted back, "We are not afraid of your expansionist ways. We will defend our homes and culture." But the wolf huffed and puffed and blew down the house of straw. The pigs ran frightened to the house of sticks. Other wolves bought up the land where the house of straw had stood and started a pig farm.

The wolf then went to the house of sticks and banged on the door. The pigs shouted back, "Leave us in peace, you flesh-eating, colonialist aggressor!" The wolf however, just smiled: "These pigs are so simple in their ideas. It would be a pity to lose them, but growth and progress must continue." So he huffed and he puffed and blew down the house of sticks. The pigs escaped and ran to the third house, the house of bricks. On the site where the house of sticks had stood, the other wolves built a luxury wellness home for wealthy, retired wolves, with indigenous souvenir shops, gambling casinos, and gourmet steak restaurants.

Finally the wolf went to the house of bricks, banging on the door and shouting, "Little pigs, little pigs, let me in!" Ignoring the wolf, the pigs sang protest songs and wrote letters to the United Nations asking for international support in their struggle for survival.

By now the wolf was becoming angrier and angrier at the pigs' opposition, so he huffed and puffed, and huffed and puffed until suddenly, screaming with pain, he fell over dead from a major heart attack caused by eating too much fatty pork. Justice had prevailed, and the three little pigs celebrated throughout the night, dancing for hours around the wolf's dead body.

The pigs then got together all the other pigs that had been terrorised by the wolves and together this porcine army attacked the wolves to free all their compatriots. After their decisive victory, they set up a model social democrat pigocracy offering free schools, free health care for all and cheap homes for all pigs.

And they all lived happily ever after!

© Ernst Klett Sprachen GmbH, Stuttgart 2011
Photocopiable
ISBN 978-3-12-534645-1

Murphy's Law

Task 1) *Match the halves to make examples of Murphy's Law.*

1. The colder the X-ray table, ○	○ a) the better it looks.
2. The farther away the future is, ○	○ b) the fewer mistakes one makes.
3. The less you enjoy serving on committees ○	○ c) the greater the chance of failure.
4. The more complicated the plan, ○	○ d) the less often you will use it.
5. The more expensive a gadget, ○	○ e) the more likely you are to be asked to do so.
6. The slower one works, ○	○ f) the more of your body you have to place on it.
7. The sooner and in more detail ○	○ g) you announce the bad news, the better.
8. A surgeon's ability ○	○ h) is inversely proportional to the time available.
9. The severity of the itch ○	○ i) is directly proportional to the cost of the carpet.
10. The distance to the gate for your flight ○	○ j) is inversely proportional to his availability.
11. The length of a meeting increases ○	○ k) is inversely proportional to the amount of progress.
12. The length of a progress report ○	○ l) is inversely proportional to the reach.
13. The life expectancy of a house plant ○	○ m) varies inversely with its price and its ugliness.
14. The chance of the bread falling with the ○ buttered side down,	○ n) with the square of the number of people attending.

Task 2) *Fill in the correct word from the box to make more examples of Murphy's Law.*

1. _Any_____ piece of cloth cut to length will be too short.

2. _____ who is unpopular is bound to be disliked.

3. _____ is possible if you don't know what you are talking about.

4. _____ as you sit down to a cup of coffee, your boss will ask you to do something.

5. _____ get mad, get even.

6. _____ shouts loudest gets the floor.

7. _____ a minute is depends on which side of the bathroom door you are.

8. _____ you want a loan, you must first prove you don't need it.

9. _____ ask a barber if you need a haircut.

10. _____ which way you ride, it's always uphill and against the wind.

11. _____ listens to you until you make a mistake.

12. _____ is impossible for a man who doesn't have to do it himself.

13. _____ you trip over your shoes do you start picking them up.

14. _____ intelligence on the planet is constant. The population is growing.

15. _____ you don't do is always more important than what you do.

16. _____ a body is immersed in water, the phone will ring.

17. _____ you turn on the radio, you hear the last notes of your favourite song.

18. _____ there's a will, there's a won't.

19. _____ carousel you stand by, your baggage will come in on another one.

20. _____ has the gold makes the rules.

Never
Whichever
When
If
No matter
Where
Anything
Only when
Whenever
How long
Anyone
~~Any~~
He who
Don't
Nobody
The sum of
What
Whoever
As soon
Nothing

© Ernst Klett Sprachen GmbH, Stuttgart 2011
Photocopiable
ISBN 978-3-12-534645-1

Oxymorons

Task 1) *Why might some people think the words in the following phrases do not belong together?*

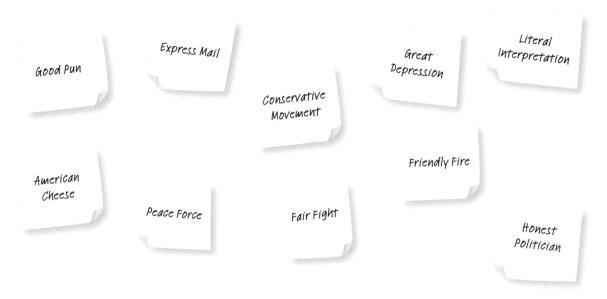

Good Pun

Express Mail

Conservative Movement

Great Depression

Literal Interpretation

American Cheese

Peace Force

Fair Fight

Friendly Fire

Honest Politician

Task 2) *Take one word from each of the two columns to make similar oxymorons.*

1. Adult	a) Group
2. Airline	b) Male
3. Civil	c) Schedule
4. Common	d) Science
5. Government	e) Secret
6. Long	f) Sense
7. Open	g) Shorts
8. Political	h) Television
9. Reality	i) War
10. Self-help	j) Worker

Task 3) *Choose a word from the box to complete the following oxymorons.*

Bush	Differences	Flight	Peace	War
Copy	~~Ethics~~	Intelligence	Tolerance	Works

1. Congressional *Ethics*

2. Holy _____

3. Microsoft _____

4. Mideast _____

5. Military _____

6. Mutual _____

7. Non-Stop _____

8. Original _____

9. President _____

10. Religious _____

© Ernst Klett Sprachen GmbH, Stuttgart 2011
Photocopiable
ISBN 978-3-12-534645-1

Klett

Playing with Words

Tom Swiftly I

A "Tom Swiftly" (or Tom Swifty) is a sentence in which a statement is linked by a pun to the manner in which it is said, e.g. "Hurry up and get to the <u>back of the ship</u>," Tom said <u>sternly</u>. The name originates from the <u>Tom Swift</u> series of books. The author tried to avoid constantly using the verb "said" by adopting a similar verb or adding an adverb.

Tom Swiftly is a fun way of extending the learners' lexical repertoire and at the same time enhancing their language awareness. It is a good way of showing how to play with words in English.

Copymaster I offers two matching tasks with the "said + adverb" type of Tom Swiftly.

Copymaster II offers one matching task with the "verb" type plus a creative activity where the learners have to find an appropriate sentence to go with the adverb.

Copymaster III provides a creative activity where the appropriate adverb has to be found (with the assistance of the first few letters of the word), and a final matching exercise based on famous people (writers, composers, etc.).

- After doing the exercises, it is a good idea to have a follow-up activity where the learners make their own sentences using the normal meaning of each of the words. Such creative exercises improve the learning effect. And if the class then compare the sentences they have made, the learners are even more likely to remember the words.

- Some words are a little more remote, which provides an opportunity for an awareness-raising exercise, for example by asking the learners to decide which of the words in each of the tasks they think it might be useful or less useful to learn. They should then be encouraged to make sentences from the more useful words. Whenever necessary they can make use of dictionaries. With some classes it may be a good idea to do only Task 1 and leave the second task on the page to a later lesson. Alternatively, teachers may wish to go on to do some of the examples of Task 2 in class and leave the remaining items for homework.

- In the creative activities there is often more than one possibility, the answers given in the Key being merely suggestions. Any sentences produced by the learners that are semantically feasible should be accepted.

- Suggest the learners proceed as follows: first look at the adverbs, think of possible contexts and then devise a sentence. Do the first one (possibly two) as an example, e.g. "Where do you have hearts?" = A game of cards = "I only have diamonds, clubs and spades," Tom said heartlessly.

They Never Die

"They Never Die" is a word game based on groups of people and what finally happens to them. They never actually die, but in some way the activity of the group comes to an end based on a pun connected with their name.

Refer to Page 6 for basic ways of working with the copymasters.

Copymaster I consists of two matching activities based on collocations with "lose" and "go" respectively, and one creative task where the appropriate groups have to be found. To stimulate the learners' imagination ask questions like "What do you associate with (balance)?", "Who (checks out)?", etc. Task 3 is a creative exercise where the learners have to suggest which group of people might suffer the various final activities. Offer prompts where necessary (e.g. "Who is sometimes the murderer in detective stores?").

Copymaster II offers in Task 1 a two-part multiple-choice activity with one difference. Both options are correct. Do the first one together with the whole class without mentioning this. Ask the class to justify the version they have chosen and then explain that both are correct. Ask the groups to explain the two versions and then choose which of the two options they prefer. Task 2 is a normal matching exercise.

The End of the Road

These two sheets are based on the use of prefixes (first *de-* and *dis-*, and then *ex-*, *out-* and *un-*). They are combined with words semantically connected with some aspect of the various occupations to produce a verb which normally has a meaning in its own right. However here it is a play on words to describe how this group might end up (the end of the road). The exercise is useful for enhancing learners' awareness of the use of prefixes and for extending vocabulary in general.

Copymaster I starts with a simple matching exercise in Task 1. Task 2 requires the learners to speculate on which group the dis- and de- words might refer to and Task 3 requires them to suggest what fate the various groups might suffer. Where necessary, offer prompting questions (e. g. "Who might be members of a band?") to start them off. They should always be asked to give reasons for their answers.

Copymaster II provides two matching exercises using all of the five prefixes. To finish off, a dictionary-based activity is offered. Each group has to find similar verbs with prefixes from a dictionary to give to other groups. They in turn have to make their own appropriate sentences for that verb.

Authors

These activities consist of combinations of book titles and authors' names. All names have some semantic connection with the title and topic of the individual books. These are sometimes hidden in words which are spelled differently but sound the same.

Copymaster I offers two matching tasks to illustrate the basic principle. Task 3 requires the learners to complete the names of the authors of the various books. Prompt when necessary with questions like: "If it's not hot, what could it be?" OR "What other word sounds similar?" There may be alternative appropriate suggestions depending on the creativity of the class. So as not to dampen the spirits of the learners, all suggestions that can be considered suitable should be accepted.

Copymaster II provides two creative tasks. In Task 1 the learners have to complete the name of the author, and in Task 2 they have to suggest a possible book title for each of the authors. Use prompting questions wherever necessary.

Tom Swiftly I

Task 1) *Find the adverb to go with the statement.*

1.	"Let's get married," said Tom …	o o a) superficially.
2.	"I think I've twisted my ankle," Tom said …	o o b) speechlessly.
3.	"I'm lost for words," Tom said …	o o c) rashly.
4.	"I've hidden the light bulbs," Tom said …	o o d) nonplussed.
5.	"I've lost my shoes", said Tom …	o o e) lamely.
6.	"Keep away, I've got measles," Tom said …	o o f) hoarsely.
7.	"My sore throat is painful," said Tom …	o o g) heatedly.
8.	"Turn down the thermostat," Tom said …	o o h) engagingly.
9.	"Don't worry, I can't add up either," Tom said …	o o i) defeatedly.
10.	"That's a very large cod," said Tom …	o o j) darkly.
11.	"Don't you work here regularly?" asked Tom …	o o k) deliberately.
12.	"I hate feminists," Tom said …	o o l) casually.

Task 2) *Find suitable adverbs from the box to complete the following statements.*

1. "We have no bananas," Tom said *fruitlessly*.

2. "This is the Netherlands," Tom stated _____.

3. "My investments are worth more every day," said Tom _____.

4. "I'm waiting for the leap year," Tom said _____.

5. "I lost my job," said Tom _____.

6. "I gave the donkey some vinegar," said Tom _____.

7. "It's too dark to see anything," said Tom _____.

8. "Don't you dare sweeten that lemon juice," said Tom _____.

9. "I've got a doctor's appointment in seven days," Tom said _____.

10. "Don't needle me," Tom said _____.

11. "Drop the gun," Tom said _____.

12. "Turn off the air-conditioning," Tom said _____.

13. "That large African animal looks horrible," Tom said _____.

14. "The performance of classical music has been cancelled," Tom said _____.

15. "That's the difference between an infinitive and a gerund," Tom said _____.

acidly
appreciatively
bitterly
disarmingly
disappointedly
delightedly
flatly
~~fruitlessly~~
icily
lackadaisically
pointedly
weakly
knowingly
disconcertingly
hypocritically

© Ernst Klett Sprachen GmbH, Stuttgart 2011
Photocopiable
ISBN 978-3-12-534645-1

Tom Swiftly II

Task 1) *Match statement and verb.*

1. "I teach at a university," Tom …   o   o a) snapped.
2. "I'm losing my hair," Tom …   o   o b) reported.
3. "I'm taking this ship back into harbour," Tom …   o   o c) repeated.
4. "May I become a chorister?" Tom …   o   o d) remarked.
5. "OK, you can borrow it again," Tom …   o   o e) relented.
6. "Pete! PETE!!" Tom …   o   o f) relayed.
7. "I used to be a paratrooper," Tom …   o   o g) rehearsed.
8. "The exit is right there," Tom …   o   o h) professed.
9. "The hen has produced another egg," Tom …   o   o i) pondered.
10. "There's no need for silence," Tom …   o   o j) pointed out.
11. "There's room for one more," Tom …   o   o k) inquired.
12. "What are you taking pictures of?" Tom …   o   o l) explained.
13. "Where shall I plant these water-lilies?" Tom …   o   o m) bawled.
14. "I've decided to change your grade," Tom's teacher … o   o n) allowed.
15. "It's time for the second funeral," Tom …   o   o o) agreed.
16. "This is my eighth doughnut, too, " Tom …   o   o p) admitted.

Task 2) *What might Tom have said in the following ways?*

1. _____ heartlessly.

2. _____ presently.

3. _____ periodically.

4. _____ unreservedly.

5. _____ independently.

6. _____ patiently.

7. _____ sternly.

8. _____ alarmingly.

9. _____ originally.

10. _____ thinly.

11. _____ doggedly.

12. _____ sagely.

© Ernst Klett Sprachen GmbH, Stuttgart 2011
Photocopiable
ISBN 978-3-12-534645-1

Klett

Tom Swiftly III

Task 1) *Find a suitable adverb to explain how Tom might have said the following sentences.*

1. "I haven't developed my photographs yet," said Tom neg*atively*.

2. "I've got to fix the automobile," said Tom mech_____.

3. "A million thanks, Monsieur," said Tom merc_____.

4. "Do you know the location?" asked Tom wari_____.

5. "I need to go on a diet," said Tom wast_____.

6. "I didn't see that French 'No Smoking' sign," fumed Tom defe_____.

7. "I like camping," said Tom inte_____.

8. "I have had too many children," said Tom over_____.

9. "I'm just an ordinary soldier," Tom admitted pri_____.

10. "We've run out of spices," Tom said gin_____.

11. "That's a beautiful mirror," Tom said ref_____.

12. "Our au-pair girl has been kidnapped," Tom said mis_____.

Task 2) *Match.*

1. "Carmen is my favorite opera," said Tom …	o	o a) the lady chattily.
2. "I can do an excellent impression of Sinatra," said Tom, being …	o	o b) bountifully.
3. "I love the novels of D. H. Lawrence," said …	o	o c) often barked.
4. "I never play any music by Hungarian composers," said Tom …	o	o d) hardily.
5. "I'm tired of smiling all the time," Lisa …	o	o e) listlessly.
6. "I've been listening to the Brandenberg Concertos," Tom …	o	o f) rejoiced.
7. "I've been listening to the Tales of Hoffmann," Tom …	o	o g) disarmingly.
8. "Once upon a time there was a beautiful princess," Tom began …	o	o h) candidly.
9. "Yes, I have been reading Voltaire," Tom admitted …	o	o i) busily.
10. "This is mutiny!" said Tom …	o	o j) perfectly frank.
11. "This statue looks like the Venus de Milo," Tom said …	o	o k) swiftly.
12. "Have you read 'Dorian Gray'?" Tom asked …	o	o l) barked.
13. "I read Gulliver's Travels when I was a child," Tom said…	o	o m) grimly.
14. "Don't rest on your laurels," Tom said …	o	o n) moaned.
15. "I've just finished reading 'Finnigan's Wake'," Tom said…	o	o o) wildly.

© Ernst Klett Sprachen GmbH, Stuttgart 2011
Photocopiable
ISBN 978-3-12-534645-1

They Never Die I

Old maths teachers never die.

They just no longer see the point.

Task 1) *These people never die, but what do they lose?*

1. Old actors never die, they simply lose…
2. Old bankers never die, they just lose…
3. Old bookkeepers never die, they just lose…
4. Old chauffeurs never die, they just lose…
5. Old computer people never die, they just lose…
6. Old dentists never die, they just lose…
7. Old electricians never die, they just lose…
8. Old engineers never die, they just lose…
9. Old librarians never die, they just lose…
10. Old newspaper editors never die, they just lose…
11. Old professors never die, they just lose…
12. Old shoe makers never die, they just lose…
13. Old soccer players never die, they just lose…
14. Old surgeons never die, they just lose…
15. Old teachers never die, they just lose…
16. Old wrestlers never die, they just lose…

a) contact.
b) interest.
c) their bearings.
d) their circulation.
e) their class.
f) their drive.
g) their faculties.
h) their figures.
i) their grip.
j) their kick.
k) their memory.
l) their patience.
m) their parts.
n) their pull.
o) their references.
p) their soul.

Task 2) *These people never die, but where do they go?*

1. Old astronauts never die, they just go *to another planet* _____.
2. Old cannibals never die, they just go _____.
3. Old Eskimos never die, they just go _____.
4. Old farmers never die, they just go _____.
5. Old geometry teachers never die, they just go _____.
6. Old internet experts never die, they just go _____.
7. Old limbo dancers never die, they just go _____.
8. Old musicians never die, they just go _____.
9. Old pacifists never die, they just go _____.
10. Old pilots never die, they just go _____.
11. Old plumbers never die, they just go _____.
12. Old publishers never die, they just go _____.

cold
down the drain
from bar to bar
off at a tangent
off people
off-line
out of print
to a higher plane
to another world
to pieces
to seed
under

Task 3) *What groups of people might suffer the following fates?*

1. They just lose their balance.
2. They just check out.
3. They just lose their appeal.
4. They just burn up.
5. They just decompose.
6. They just stop developing.
7. They just derail.
8. They just go downhill fast.
9. They just achieve their final goal.
10. They just wind down.

© Ernst Klett Sprachen GmbH, Stuttgart 2011
Photocopiable
ISBN 978-3-12-534645-1

Klett

Old churchmen never die.

They just lose their organs.

They Never Die II

Task 1) *The following groups don't die, but what do they do? Tick (✓) the right box.*

	A	B
1. Old soldiers with medals never die, they just get…	☐ deserved	☐ discouraged
2. Old car mechanics never die, they just get…	☐ debooted	☐ retired
3. Old conductors never die, they just get…	☐ denoted	☐ disconcerted
4. Old Eskimos never die, they just get…	☐ cold feet	☐ de-iced
5. Old fishermen never die, they just get…	☐ descaled	☐ reel tired
6. Old footballers never die, they just get…	☐ mismatched	☐ offside
7. Old geologists never die, they just get…	☐ reminded	☐ stoned
8. Old journalists never die, they just get…	☐ depressed	☐ misprinted
9. Old librarians never die, they just get…	☐ rebound	☐ re-shelved
10. Old magicians never die, they just get…	☐ misspelled	☐ disillusioned
11. Old statisticians never die, they just get…	☐ disfigured	☐ broken down by age and sex
12. Old students never die, they just get…	☐ remarked	☐ degraded

Task 2) *What happens to the following groups of people?*

1. Old barmen never die, they just… o	o a) become mothballed.
2. Old beekeepers never die, they just… o	o b) become nonplussed.
3. Old biscuit makers never die, they just… o	o c) become unstrung.
4. Old blondes never fade, they just… o	o d) buzz off.
5. Old burglars never die, they just… o	o e) don't give a hoot.
6. Old cleaning people never die, they just… o	o f) dye away.
7. Old environmentalists never die, they are just… o	o g) end up crackers.
8. Old flower growers never die, they just… o	o h) end up in a jam.
9. Old Helsinki tourists never die, they just… o	o i) end up on the rocks!
10. Old herbalists never die, they just… o	o j) kick the bucket.
11. Old mathematicians never die, they just… o	o k) lose the habit.
12. Old nuns never die, they just… o	o l) recycled.
13. Old owls never die, they just… o	o m) retire to their beds.
14. Old strawberry growers never die, they just… o	o n) run out of thyme.
15. Old tailors never die, they just… o	o o) steal away.
16. Old violinists never die, they just… o	o p) vanish into Finn Air.

© Ernst Klett Sprachen GmbH, Stuttgart 2011
Photocopiable
ISBN 978-3-12-534645-1

The End of the Road I – De and Dis

Task 1) *What might happen to these groups? Match.*

1. Authors
2. Bullfighters
3. Calendar makers
4. Church goers
5. Computer programmers
6. Male underwear makers
7. Traffic wardens
8. Wallet manufacturers

a) debriefed
b) defiled
c) defined
d) described
e) discharged
f) dismayed
g) dispersed
h) dissected

Task 2) *Who might be…?*

Dis-

1. disbanded – *jazz musicians*

2. discarded – _____

3. disfigured – _____

4. discredited – _____

5. disgruntled – _____

6. disappointed – _____

7. dismissed – _____

De-

8. detailed – *horses*

9. degraded – _____

10. demeaned – _____

11. derided – _____

12. descaled – _____

13. deserved – _____

14. detested – _____

Task 3) *What fate might the following groups suffer?*

De-

1. Striptease artists – *defrocked*

2. Butchers – _____

3. Poultry farmers – _____

4. Politicians – _____

5. Electricians – _____

6. Songwriters – _____

7. Pedicure experts – _____

8. Software developers – _____

Dis-

9. US males – *disguised*

10. Adult literacy students – _____

11. British coin collectors – _____

12. Facilitators – _____

13. Meteorologists – _____

14. Club secretaries – _____

15. Savings banks – _____

16. Members of the House of Lords – _____

© Ernst Klett Sprachen GmbH, Stuttgart 2011
Photocopiable
ISBN 978-3-12-534645-1

Klett

The End of the Road II – De, Dis, Ex, Out and Un

Task 1) *What might happen to these groups? Match.*

1.	Airline passengers are …	o	o a) exchanged.
2.	Contract breakers are …	o	o b) explained.
3.	Diary keepers are …	o	o c) expounded.
4.	English bankers are …	o	o d) exterminated.
5.	Foreign currency dealers are …	o	o e) extolled.
6.	French composers are …	o	o f) outcast.
7.	Fashion designers are …	o	o g) outclassed.
8.	Martians are …	o	o h) outdated.
9.	Novelists are …	o	o i) outsmarted.
10.	Road charge collectors are …	o	o j) outsourced.
11.	Tailors are …	o	o k) unauthorized.
12.	Teachers are …	o	o l) unearthed.
13.	The actors in a play are …	o	o m) unmanned.
14.	Tomato ketchup producers are …	o	o n) unravelled.
15.	Wives are …	o	o o) unsuited.

Task 2) *Make sentences using the prefix and one of the words in the box.*

1. Botanists are *deflowered*_____. (de)

2. Cannibal victims are _____. (dis)

3. Castle owners are _____. (de)

4. Symphony conductors are _____. (dis)

5. Dog owners are _____. (un)

6. English bankers are _____. (ex)

7. Language learners are _____. (out)

8. Nurses are _____. (ex)

9. Telephonists are _____. (dis)

10. Prisoners are _____. (ex)

11. Referees are _____. (un)

12. Sandwich makers are _____. (out)

13. Statisticians are _____. (out)

celled
~~flowered~~
heartened
matched
connected
moted
numbered
pounded
spoken
spread
tended
leashed
concerted

© Ernst Klett Sprachen GmbH, Stuttgart 2011
Photocopiable
ISBN 978-3-12-534645-1

Authors I

Task 1) *Match the books with the authors.*

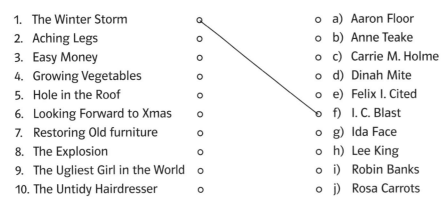

1. The Winter Storm	o	o a) Aaron Floor
2. Aching Legs	o	o b) Anne Teake
3. Easy Money	o	o c) Carrie M. Holme
4. Growing Vegetables	o	o d) Dinah Mite
5. Hole in the Roof	o	o e) Felix I. Cited
6. Looking Forward to Xmas	o	o f) I. C. Blast
7. Restoring Old furniture	o	o g) Ida Face
8. The Explosion	o	o h) Lee King
9. The Ugliest Girl in the World	o	o i) Robin Banks
10. The Untidy Hairdresser	o	o j) Rosa Carrots

Task 2) *Find the authors of the following books.*

1. An Introduction to Astrology	o	o Alec o		o Arronnie
2. Archery for Beginners:	o	o Beau o		o Fraide
3. First Aid for Beginners	o	o Dusty o		o Kope
4. Good Teachers	o	o Emma o		o Lott
5. Holidays off the Beaten Track	o	o Horace o		o N. Arrers
6. Italian Cuisine	o	o Mac o		o O'Kaye
7. Safety in the Home	o	o Maggie o		o Rhodes
8. Successful Presidents	o	o Noah o		o Seins
9. The Ghost Train	o	o Polly o		o Tishens
10. Weekly Entertainment	o	o R.U. o		o Trishun

Task 3) *Complete the name of the author.*

1. "Could be Hotter" by Luke *Warm* _____

2. "A Life of Luxury" by Millie _____

3. "The Simple Things in Life" by Rudy _____

4. "Pre-digital Watches" by Anna _____

5. "Going up in the World" by Ellie _____

6. "Garden Chairs" by Patty O' _____

7. "Holiday Places for the Family" by Sandie _____

8. "I Hate My Husband" by Ivana D. _____

9. "Cooking Spaghetti" by Al _____

10. "My Favourite Instrument" by Amanda _____

11. "Quotations from Shakespeare" by Toby _____

12. "Fixing Computer Problems" by Dee _____

13. "Jokes to Annoy Your Friends" by Terry _____

14. "French Cars" by Myra _____

15. "Government Statements" by Lotte _____

16. "Regular Exercise" by Jim _____

© Ernst Klett Sprachen GmbH, Stuttgart 2011
Photocopiable
ISBN 978-3-12-534645-1

Klett

Authors II

Task 1) *Complete the name of the author.*

1. "Hot Dog" by Frank *Furter* _____

2. "New Words" by Dick _____

3. "100 Years Old Today" by Abbie _____

4. "What a Surprise!" by Oliver _____

5. "Travelling in China" by Rick _____

6. "Seasickness" by Gayle _____

7. "The Problem of Apathy" by Hu _____

8. "Army Prisons" by Corporal _____

9. "The Best Police Force" by Scott _____

10. "How to Stop Smoking" by Will _____

11. "Tolstoy's Life Story" by Warren _____

12. "Why Take Out Insurance?" by Justin _____

13. "Military Rule" by Marshall _____

14. "Split Personalities" by Jacqueline _____

15. "Outdoor Meals" by Alf _____

16. "Out of Work" by Anita _____

Task 2) *What topic might the following authors have written a book about? Suggest a title for the book.*

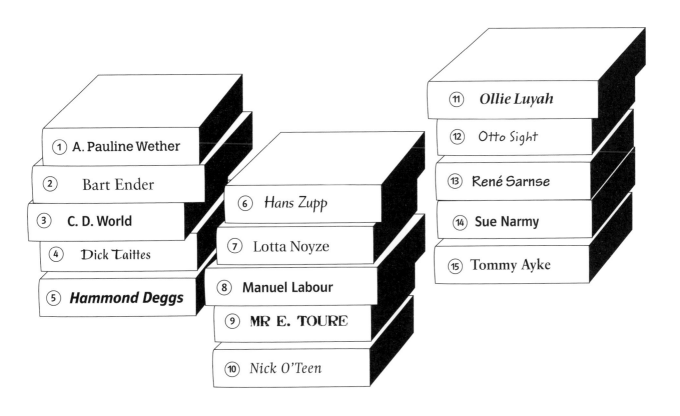

1. A. Pauline Wether
2. Bart Ender
3. C. D. World
4. Dick Taittes
5. **Hammond Deggs**
6. Hans Zupp
7. Lotta Noyze
8. **Manuel Labour**
9. MR E. TOURE
10. Nick O'Teen
11. **Ollie Luyah**
12. Otto Sight
13. René Sarnse
14. **Sue Narmy**
15. Tommy Ayke

© Ernst Klett Sprachen GmbH, Stuttgart 2011
Photocopiable
ISBN 978-3-12-534645-1

Classic Native-Speaker Mistakes

Spoonerisms

Spoonerisms are phrases in which the initial consonants or sounds of two consecutive words have been swapped round, creating an amusing new expression. The name comes from the Revd. W. A. Spooner (1844–1930), who was the Warden of New College, Oxford. He was famous for a number of mistakes like the accusation that a student had "hissed my mystery lectures". Most of these errors were most probably simple slips of the tongue, but quite a few of the spoonerisms quoted in books are probably his. More details about the Revd W. A. Spooner and spoonerisms can be found in Wikipedia.

The spoonerism tasks offered here are mainly fun activities but they are quite useful for promoting language awareness in terms of sounds and spelling. **Copymaster I** contains two correction tasks where it is recommended to make sure the learners understand how spoonerisms work, in particular the way that the same sounds can produce different spellings. Task 3 is similar but uses geographical names.

Copymaster II is based on a traditional fairy tale "Little Red Riding Hood". The first half of the story has been spoonerised, and the task is to put the story back into normal English. The second half of the story has been left in the original and the class, working in groups, have to attempt to spoonerise the story. After the groups have finished, they should read out their spoonerised version to the whole class.

Malapropisms

The name malapropism comes from Mrs. Malaprop, a character in the play "The Rivals" written by Richard Brinsley Sheridan in 1775. Malapropisms are mistakes made when the word or phrase used sounds similar to the word the speaker or writer intended to use, but means something different. Such malapropisms can be made deliberately for comic effect or are mistakes made in the heat of the moment. The name Mrs Malaprop comes from the French phrase malapropos which means inappropriate. And Mrs Malaprop makes a number of such mistakes throughout the play.

Malapropisms are committed everyday by public speakers when the "tongue is faster than the brain" and are often made by sports reporters during live commentaries. The tasks provided here are useful for vocabulary work, especially in examples that require the precise word.

Copymaster I offers in Tasks 1 and 2 correction activities taken from Sheridan's play. Task 3 provides a number of examples of the type of mistakes President George W. Bush often made in free spontaneous speech, the task being to make correct sentences from each of the examples.

Copymaster II offers a matching exercise (Task 1) based on typical errors made by people involved in sports, particularly football. Task 2 is an interpretation exercise which contains a number of examples that Donald Rumsfeld, who was Secretary of Defense during the Iraq war in 2003, produced in press conferences in order to try to hide what was really happening in the Iraq conflict. These sentences do not really contain mistakes. They are deliberately intended to be as imprecise and evasive as possible and are good illustrations of how politicians in particular use vagueness strategies in order to avoid telling the (whole) truth. For this reason, the sentences are not intended to be corrected. The task is to discuss what Rumsfeld is saying and what he is trying to hide.

Howlers

In British English, howlers are mistakes that are so funny that people hearing them "howl with laughter". It is often used to refer to mistakes made in school examinations. These mistakes can be examples of the wrong use of a word or where definitions are wrong or where the content is wrong.

Task 1 is a correction activity where the wrong word or phrase needs to be found and corrected. In Task 2, learners have to provide the correct definition for each of the words. When the groups read out their definitions, check they are understandable (correct only when the errors hinder comprehension).

The howlers in Task 3 are not for correction. The learners have to discuss and explain why the statements are howlers and why they are amusing.

Letters

All the letters in this section have actually been written to Government departments and car insurance companies. They contain typical errors made by native speakers who are either unused to writing letters or who have not enjoyed a very high standard of education.

Copymaster I contains a correction exercise (Task 1) as an introduction to the type of language mistake made in such letters, followed by a guessing task (Task 2) where the learners discuss and speculate why the letter was written and what the writer wants the addressee to do. This can be done together with the whole class with individual learners calling out ideas.

Copymaster II offers another guessing activity (Task 1) which requires the learners to speculate on the background to the letter. After each report the class can decide which version is the most realistic. Task 2 is a gap-filling activity based on letters to car insurance companies who are trying to avoid being blamed for an accident that they have been involved in.

Refer to Page 6 for basic ways of working with the copymasters.

> Hi,
> My name is Jack I accidently hit your car & someone saw me so I'm pretending to write down my details.
>
> Sorry,
> Jack

Spoonerisms I

Task 1) *What did the speakers intend to say? Write the correct version in the spaces provided.*

1. A blushing crow   A cr<u>ushing</u> b<u>low</u>

2. I must mend the sail.   I must s_____ the m_____.

3. You've tasted two worms.   You've w_____ two t_____.

4. It crawls through the fax.   It f_____ through the cr_____.

5. Fighting a liar.   L_____ a f_____.

6. Know your blows.   B_____ your n_____.

7. Go and shake a tower.   Go and t_____ a sh_____.

8. You have very mad banners.   You have very b_____ m_____.

9. A lack of pies.   A p_____ of l_____.

10. It's roaring with pain.   It's p_____ with _____.

Task 2) *Correct the following spoonerisms in the spaces provided.*

1. Bat flattery – *flat battery* _____
2. Bedding wells – _____
3. Chipping the flannel on TV – _____
4. Eye ball – _____
5. Fight in your race – _____
6. Flutter by – _____

7. I'm shout of the hour – _____
8. Lead of spite – _____
9. No tails – _____
10. Ready as a stock – _____
11. Soul of ballad – _____
12. Wave the sails – _____

Task 3) *What places are meant? Write the correct version in the space provided.*

1. corridor fleas *Florida Keys* _____
2. fantasy _____
3. kiss once in _____
4. whirlin' ball _____
5. lark isle _____

6. hassle coward _____
7. worn call _____
8. men (dark) _____
9. least undone _____
10. bridge alter _____

© Ernst Klett Sprachen GmbH, Stuttgart 2011
Photocopiable
ISBN 978-3-12-534645-1

Klett

Spoonerisms II

Task 1) Read the following fairy-tale and put it into normal English.

Tunce upon a wime there lived in a virtain cillage a little guntry curl, the grittiest pearl that was ever seen. Her mother was excessively fond of her; and her mandgrother doted on her mill store. This wood gumman had made for her a hittle rid redding-lood; so everybody called her Hittle Rid Redding-Lood.

Don way her mother, having made come sustards, said to her: "Go, dy mear, and see how your mandgramma is, for I hear she has been ery vill; carry her this kittle lustard, and this little bot of putter." Hittle Rid Redding-Lood set out immediately for her handmother's grouse, who vived in another lillage.

As she was woing through the good, she met a warge lolf, who asked gere she was whoing. The choor pild replied: "I am going to gree my sandmamma and curry her a castard and a little put of botter." "Does she live a wong lay away?" said the wolf. "Oh, yes," replied Hittle Rid Redding-Lood; "it is meyond that bill you see there, it's the hirst vouse in the fillage."

The bolf wegan to fun as rast as he could, taking the wortest shay, and the gittle lirl walked slowly, nathering guts, running after flutterbies, and baking mouquets of flittle lowers. The Wolf got to the old homan's wouse first and docked at the noor--tap, tap.

"Tho's where?" "Your chandgrild," replied the Wolf, speaking in Hittle Rid Redding-Lood's voice; "I've cought you a brustard and a pittle bot of lutter from ma mymma."

The mandgrother cried out: "Just dush the poor and come in." The Wolf dopened the or, and then fell upon the wood goman and ate her up in a moment. He then dut the shoor and went into the bandmother's gred.

Task 2) Now "spoonerise" the rest of the story.

Some time afterward Little Red Riding-Hood knocked at the door. "Who's there?" Little Red Riding-Hood heard the big voice of the Wolf, and believing her grandmother had got a cold, answered: "It's me, Little Red Riding-Hood, who has brought you a custard and a little pot of butter from mamma." She opened the door and went into the house.

The big Wolf, hiding himself under the bed-clothes said: "Put the custard and the little pot of butter upon the stool."

Little Red Riding-Hood went to the bed, and said to her grandmother: "Grandmamma, what great arms you have got!" "All the better to hug you, my dear." "Grandmamma, what great ears you have got!" "All the better to hear you, my child." "Grandmamma, what great eyes you have got!" "All the better to see you, my child." "Grandmamma, what great teeth you have got!" " All the better to eat you."

And, saying these words, the wicked wolf fell upon Little Red Riding-Hood, and ate her all up.

© Ernst Klett Sprachen GmbH, Stuttgart 2011
Photocopiable
ISBN 978-3-12-534645-1

Malapropisms I

Task 1) *Choose one of the words a) – e) to correct the mistakes in the following sentences.*

1. "He is the very pineapple of politeness." o
2. "His physiognomy so grammatical!" o
3. "Oh! It gives me the hydrostatics to such a degree." o
4. "She's as headstrong as an allegory on the banks of the Nile." o
5. "Why, murder's the matter! Killing's the matter! – but he can o
   tell you the perpendiculars."

   o a) alligator
   o b) hysterics
   o c) particulars
   o d) phraseology
   o e) pinnacle

Task 2) *Underline the wrong word in each of the following sentences. Write the correct word in the space provided.*

1. "O, he will <u>dissolve</u> my mystery!" – *(re)solve*

2. "I have since laid Sir Anthony's preposition before her." – _____

3. "I hope you will represent her to the captain as an object not altogether illegible." – _____

4. "I am sorry to say, Sir Anthony, that my affluence over my niece is very small." – _____

5. "I thought she had persisted from corresponding with him." – _____

6. "She might reprehend the true meaning of what she is saying." – _____

Task 3) *The following statements were made by George W. Bush. Correct the mistakes.*

1 You teach a child to read, and he or her will be able to pass a literacy test.

2 Rarely is the question asked: Is our children learning?

3 Our enemies are innovative and resourceful, and so are we. They never stop thinking about new ways to harm our country and our people, and neither do we.

4 For every fatal shooting, there were roughly three non-fatal shootings. And, folks, this is unacceptable in America. It's just unacceptable. And we're going to do something about it.

5 I can only speak to myself.

6 Anyone engaging in illegal financial transactions will be caught and persecuted.

7 One of the very difficult parts of the decision I made on the financial crisis was to use hardworking people's money to help prevent there to be a crisis.

8 And so, General, I want to thank you for your service. And I appreciate the fact that you really snatched defeat out of the jaws of those who are trying to defeat us in Iraq.

9 The same folks that are bombing innocent people in Iraq were the ones who attacked us in America on September the 11th.

10 One of my concerns is that the health care not be as good as it can possibly be.

© Ernst Klett Sprachen GmbH, Stuttgart 2011
Photocopiable
ISBN 978-3-12-534645-1

Klett

Malapropisms II

Task 1) *Football players, managers and radio commentators are well-known for 21st century "malapropisms".*
Match the two halves of each quotation.

1. "Apart from their goals,
2. "Gary always weighed up his options,
3. "He's got a knock on his shin there,
4. "I felt a lump in my throat,
5. "If I was still at Ipswich,
6. "It's 60-40 against him being fit,
7. "I've had an interest in racing all my life,
8. "The Germans only have one player under 22,
9. "Unless the chairman decides to sack me,
10. "We must have had 99 per cent of the match,
11. "Well, either side could win it,
12. "What I said to them at half time

a) and he's 23."
b) as the ball went in."
c) but he's got half a chance."
d) especially when he had no choice."
e) I won't be quitting."
f) I wouldn't be where I am today."
g) it was the other three per cent that cost us."
h) just above the knee."
i) Norway haven't scored."
j) or it could be a draw."
k) or longer really."
l) would be unprintable on the radio."

Task 2) *The following statements were made by Donald Rumsfeld during the 2003 Iraq War. What do you think he wanted to say?*

2. I would not say that the future is necessarily less predictable than the past. I think the past was not predictable when it started.

1. We do know of certain knowledge that Osama Bin Laden is either in Afghanistan, or in some other country, or dead.

3. Reports that say that something hasn't happened are always interesting to me, because as we know, there are known knowns; there are things we know we know. We also know there are known unknowns; that is to say we know there are some things we do not know. But there are also unknown unknowns -- the ones we don't know we don't know.

4. There's another way to phrase that and that is that the absence of evidence is not the evidence of absence. It is basically saying the same thing in a different way. Simply because you do not have evidence that something does exist, does not mean that you have evidence that it doesn't exist.

5. If I know the answer, I'll tell you the answer, and if I don't, I'll just respond, cleverly.

6. I believe what I said yesterday. I don't know what I said, but I know what I think, and, well, I assume it's what I said.

7. Needless to say, the President is correct. Whatever it was he said.

8. As you know, you go to war with the army you have, not the army you might want or wish to have at a later time.

9. He is either alive and well or alive and not too well or not alive.

© Ernst Klett Sprachen GmbH, Stuttgart 2011
Photocopiable
ISBN 978-3-12-534645-1

Howlers

Task 1) *Underline and correct the wrong words in the following sentences taken from school exam papers.*

1. <u>Orange tans</u> are an endangered species.
2. The house was old, empty and abundant.
3. His Heinous King Henry VIII.
4. A coma is a punctual mark like a full stop.
5. A magnet is something found in a bad apple.
6. Dead people are buried in a symmetry.
7. A turbine is what an Arab wears on his head.
8. Adolescence is the stage between puberty and adultery.
9. Darwin wrote the Organ of the Species.
10. Louis Pasteur discovered a cure for rabbis.
11. Oysters are only eligible in the winter.
12. Julius Caesar extinguished himself on the battlefields of Gaul.
13. You give a momentum to a guest when they leave.
14. Monotony is being married to the same person all your life.
15. Patriarchy treats women as escape goats.
16. People should not serve food if they are deceased.
17. The equator is a menagerie line that runs around the world.
18. Bach practiced his music on an old spinster who lived in the attic.
19. When you get old, you become intercontinental.
20. The U.S have highly developed marital equipment.

Task 2) *The following definitions are wrong. Replace the underlined words. Write the correct definitions for these words on a separate piece of paper.*

1. A <u>vacuum</u> is a large empty space where the Pope lives.
2. An <u>octogenarian</u> is an animal which has eight young at birth.
3. Ancient Egypt was inhabited by mummies and they all wrote in <u>hydraulics</u>.
4. <u>Effluent</u> means fluent in English as a Foreign Language.
5. <u>Germination</u> is the process of becoming a German.
6. <u>Migration</u> is a headache that birds get when they fly south for the winter.
7. <u>Romans</u> were so called because they never stayed in one place for very long.
8. The most influential aspect of poverty is the absence of <u>marriage</u> between parents, particularly mothers.
9. <u>Unleavened</u> bread is bread made without any ingredients.
10. A <u>polygon</u> is a dead parrot.
11. An <u>anglophile</u> is a person who likes fishing.
12. <u>Ambiguous</u> means having two wives and not being able to change this.

Task 3) *Explain why these statements are howlers.*

1. Milton was a poet who wrote 'Paradise Lost'. When his wife died, he wrote 'Paradise Regained'.
2. Beethoven was deaf so he wrote loud music.
3. Gravity was invented by Isaac Newton. It is chiefly noticeable in the autumn.
4. Without the Greeks, we wouldn't have history.
5. In the reign of Henry VIII, the head of the Church fell into the hands of the king.
6. The brave knight was swallowed up by the awful abbess that yawned all of a sudden in front of him.
7. Our forefathers are not living as long as they used to.
8. A stand-alone computer is when you haven't got a chair to sit on.
9. A terminal illness is when you are sick at the airport.
10. Heavy water is with ships in it.

© Ernst Klett Sprachen GmbH, Stuttgart 2011
Photocopiable
ISBN 978-3-12-534645-1

Letters I

Task 1) *What is wrong in these letters? Write the correct version in the space below.*

① Dear Sir,
  ... In reply to your letter. I have already co-habited with your office, so far without result.

② Dear Sir,
  ... Please send my money at once as I have fallen into errors with my landlord.

③ Dear Sir,
  ... Regarding your enquiry the teeth in the top are alright but the ones in the bottom are hurting terribly...

④ Dear Sir,
  ... I am writing on behalf of my sink which is coming away from the wall...

1. _____

2. _____

3. _____

4. _____

Task 2) *Discuss the following letters. What did the writer want to say?*

① "I am forwarding my marriage certificate and two children, one of which is a mistake as you will see."

② "I cannot get sick pay. I have six children. Can you tell me why this is?"

③ "I have enclosed my marriage certificate and six children. I have some and one died, which was baptised on a half sheet of paper by the Rev. Thomas."

④ "I want money as quick as you can send it. I have been in bed with my doctor all week and he does not seem to be doing me any good."

⑤ "My lavatory seat is cracked – where do I stand?"

⑥ "Our lavatory seat is broken in half and is now in three pieces."

⑦ "This is my eighth child. What are you doing about it?"

⑧ "Will you please send a man to look at my water; it is a funny colour and not fit to drink."

⑨ "You have changed my little girl into a little boy. Will this make any difference?"

⑩ "Our kitchen floor is damp. We have two children and would like a third, so please send someone round to do something about it."

⑪ "The toilet is blocked and we cannot bath the children until it is cleared."

⑫ "This is to let you know that our toilet seat is broken and we can't get BBC2 television programme"

© Ernst Klett Sprachen GmbH, Stuttgart 2011
Photocopiable
ISBN 978-3-12-534645-1

Letters II

Task 1) *What do you think were the problems that led to these letters?*

1. "I am writing these lines for Mrs. Green who cannot write herself. She expects to be confined next week and can do with it."

2. "In accordance with your instructions I have given birth to twins in the enclosed envelope."

3. "In answer to your letter I have given birth to a little boy weighing ten pounds. Is this satisfactory?"

4. "Milk is wanted for my baby as the father is unable to supply it."

5. "Mrs. Brown has no clothes and has not had any for a year. The vicar has been visiting her."

6. "Please find out if my husband is dead, as the man I am now living with won't eat or do anything until he is sure."

7. "Sir, I am glad to say my husband, reported missing, is now dead."

8. "Unless I get my husband's money I shall be forced to lead an immoral life."

Task 2) *The following statements are taken from letters to insurance companies after car accidents.*

backed into	swerve	pavement
hit	stationary	collided
struck	caused	slow down
intersection	ran over	fault
~~bumped~~	accident	vehicle

1. "I _**bumped**_ into a lamp-post which was obscured by human beings."

2. "The accident was _____ by me waving to the man I hit last week."

3. "I knocked over a man; he admitted it was his _____ for he had been knocked down before."

4. "To avoid hitting the bumper of the car in front I _____ a pedestrian."

5. "I started to _____ but the traffic was more _____ than I thought."

6. "An invisible car came out of nowhere, _____ my car and vanished."

7. "My car was legally parked as it _____ another _____."

8. "The man ran for the _____, but I got him."

9. "Coming home I drove into the wrong house and _____ with a tree I don't have."

10. "The guy was all over the road. I had to _____ a number of times before I _____ him."

11. **"I had been driving for forty years when I fell asleep at the wheel and had an _____."**

12. "As I approached an _____ I suddenly a sign where there had been no stop sign before."

© Ernst Klett Sprachen GmbH, Stuttgart 2011
Photocopiable
ISBN 978-3-12-534645-1

Klett

Graffiti and Street Culture

Who Rules?

Graffiti such as "X rules, OK?" started off a "cult movement" of aggressive statements used by groups of young people, for example gangs "Skinheads rule, OK?" or various sporting groups, e.g. "Arsenal rules, OK?" which became a model for many more often humorous variations. The actual origins are not really clear, some people connecting such statements with the Glasgow gangs of the 1930's ("Agree with me and I won't hurt or kill you."). In the eighties it became a cult model for graffitists throughout the UK who used it to make in some cases outrageous puns, cf. the examples on the copymasters. The variations may be phonetic, lexical, semantic, etc.

Copymaster I: Tasks 1 and 2 are matching activities. Explain that the way to find the correct answer is to look firstly at the information given and then at the various alternatives in order to find the best match.

Copymaster II: Task 1 is a matching activity followed by Tasks 2 and 3 which are more creative tasks. Prompt where necessary.

"I used to be . . ."

These sentences are another example of a graffiti format often found on public buildings or underground stations in the UK. The humour is based on the fact that the second half of the sentence contradicts the first half. The format is a very useful way of extending learners' lexical repertoire.

Task 1 is a matching activity, whereas Tasks 2 and 3 are creative writing tasks. When the groups have finished the latter two tasks, ask each group to read out one of the second halves to the rest of the class, who then have to guess which of the words the sentence goes with. The other groups can then read out their alternatives.

One-Liners

One-liners are another typical form of graffiti consisting of two halves, the second half providing an unexpected and amusing way of completing the sentence.

Copymaster I: Task 1 is a matching exercise. Check afterwards by asking individual groups to read out the sentences they have put together. Task 2 is an unjumbling exercise where the first two to three words are given to start off the sentence. The learners have to put the jumbled words in the correct order to complete the sentence. Punctuation marks and capital letters have been given to help the learners solve the task. It is not really necessary to insist on exactly the correct word order, as understanding is the higher priority.

Copymaster II: Task 1 takes the unjumbling activity one step further by asking the learners to match the jumbled words with the openers. If this proves a little difficult for the class, simply tell them which opener goes with which jumbled sentence, and let them just do the unjumbling work. After one example, divide the class into small working groups and let them find the solutions. Check by asking the groups to read out their answers.

Refer to Page 6 for basic ways of working with the copymasters.

Rhyming Slang

In rhyming slang, words are replaced by different words that rhyme with the original, very often as part of a two-word phrase, e.g. stairs becomes "apples and pears". The second word is then sometimes omitted e.g. "I'm going up the apples", or "Sherman" for an American (Sherman tank = Yank) which can make the meaning quite difficult for the uninitiated. The exact origin of rhyming slang is unclear, but rhyming slang in England is strongly associated with Cockney speech from the East End of London. There are hundreds of examples of rhyming slang expressions, but many of these are not very well known outside the London area. The ones used in the tasks are those more frequently encountered in everyday speech all over Britain, although not all native speakers realise how and where they originated.

Task 1 is a matching exercise. The phrases refer to parts of the body and articles of clothing, the task being to draw a line to connect them to the appropriate part of the figure, whereas in Task 2 the learners have to guess what the rhyming slang phrase means. The phrases have been put into a context to help. In both tasks the teacher should do the first example together with the class to illustrate the procedure before leaving the remaining examples to small working groups. Check the solutions after each task. Note: Where the words are in brackets, this is to indicate that the bracketed word is quite often omitted.

Bingo

The game of Bingo is probably well-known to most learners. When played in public bingo halls in the UK, the callers often use a variety of different words and phrases for the numbers as they come up. This is the basis for the activities on this sheet. For the various numbers, these phrases come from various sources: television programmes, sport, songs, the shape and sound of the number, etc.

In both tasks the learners have to find the numbers that the expressions refer to by either matching the phrase and number (Task 1) or by guessing and writing the number in the space provided (Task 2). Try one or two with the whole class before asking small groups to find as many as they can. Monitor the group work closely and offer clues (cf. Key) if signs of frustration occur. Task 3 is an actual game of bingo. Ask the learners to make a bingo card with a square of 5 x 5 empty spaces. The game can be played with the whole class or in groups of about five learners. In either case, each learner can call out one of the numbers on her or his card, but they must use a rhyming slang expression. If the class is creative and likes playing Bingo, let them make their own rhyming slang.

Who Rules? I

Task 1) *Who rules? Choose the correct "rulers".*

1. Amnesia rules …   o   o a) relatively, OK - well, in theory, anyway.

2. Botanists rule …   o   o b) OK, OK, OK.

3. Bureaucracy rules …   o   o c) oak hay.

4. Einstein rules …   o   o d) ohkay.

5. Flower power rules …   o   o e) bouquet.

6. Poor spellers rule …   o   o f) …. er, ….. um …

Task 2) *Who "rules" here? Write your answers in the space provided.*

1. *Horses*_____ rule, neigh, neigh.

2. _____ rule, O K-K-K-K-K-K!

3. _____ rule, oh, gay.

4. _____ rules, UK.

5. _____ rules Bangk OK.

6. _____ rule, ole!

7. _____ rules, not OK.

8. _____ rules, O °K.

9. _____ rule, all right, acceptable, satisfactory.

10. _____ rul.

© Ernst Klett Sprachen GmbH, Stuttgart 2011
Photocopiable
ISBN 978-3-12-534645-1

Who Rules? II

Task 1) *Choose the correct endings.*

1. British trees rule … ○	○	a) … au Quai?
2. Computers rule … ○	○	b) … C2H5OK?
3. Democracy rules … ○	○	c) … [" – OK!?! – …"]
4. French dockers rule … ○	○	d) … 40% ok …45% no …15% don't know.
5. Potassium exthoxide rules … ○	○	e) … oak …eh?
6. Procrastination will rule … ○	○	f) … Och Aye!
7. Punctuation marks rule … ○	○	g) … if only for a bit …OK?
8. The Scots rule … ○	○	h) … one day …OK?

Task 2) *How do the following examples end?*

1. Anagrams rule, *or luke* _____ ?

2. Anarchy rules, _____ ?

3. Shakespeare rules, _____ ?

4. Dyslexics lure, _____ ?

5. James Bond rules, _____ ?

6. Schizophrenia rules, _____ ?

7. Rooner spules, _____ ?

8. Roget's Thesaurus rules, _____ ?

Task 3) *Who "rules" here? Write your answers in the space provided.*

1. *Morse Code* _____ rules, ···-−−-?

2. _____ rule, O'Casey?

3. _____ rule. Oh. ¿Qué?

4. _____ rule, e.g.?

5. _____ rules, BO?

6. _____ rules, if you would deign to agree with me?

7. _____ rules, ongoing agreement situation?

8. _____ rules, Tokay?

© Ernst Klett Sprachen GmbH, Stuttgart 2011
Photocopiable
ISBN 978-3-12-534645-1

Klett

Task 1) *Match the two halves.*

1. I used to be a werewolf, ...   o————o   a) ... but I'm all right noooooooooooooooooooow!
2. I used to be self-deprecating, ...   o   o   b) ... but now ...
3. I used to be apathetic, ...   o   o   c) ... but now I am absolutely perfect.
4. I used to be conceited, ...   o   o   d) ... but now I couldn't care less.
5. I used to be inattentive, ...   o   o   e) ... but now I know everything.
6. I used to be infallible, ...   o   o   f) ... but now I never make mistakes.
7. I used to be nostalgic, ...   o   o   g) ... but now we' re okay.
8. I used to be omniscient, ...   o   o   h) ... but now I'm more concerned with the past.
9. I used to be schizophrenic, ...   o   o   i) ... but now I'm not focussed enough.
10. I used to be able to finish   o   o   j) ... but now I think I'm the stupidest person in
    everything I started, ...   the world.

Task 2) *Can you make similar sentences with the following words?*

1. I used to be inconsistent, but *now I constantly change my mind* _____.

2. I used to be indispensible, but _____.

3. I used to be inquisitive, but _____.

4. I used to be insufferable, but _____.

5. I used to be irresponsible, but _____.

6. I used to be introspective, but _____.

7. I used to be gullible, but _____.

8. I used to be reticent, but _____.

9. I used to be self-indulgent, but _____.

10. I used to be mendacious, but _____.

Task 3) *Form groups. Find words in a dictionary and ask other groups to make similar sentences.*

© Ernst Klett Sprachen GmbH, Stuttgart 2011
Photocopiable
ISBN 978-3-12-534645-1

One-Liners I

Task 1) *Match the two halves.*

1. 8 of every 10 men write with a ball-point pen.	o	o a) … and ends with your arms in his sink.
2. 80% of bishops read "The Times".	o	o b) … aren't as good as yours.
3. Avoid the end of the year rush,	o	o c) … beat yourself up.
4. Beethoven was so deaf,	o	o d) … but Genghis Khan.
5. Emmanual Kant,	o	o e) … eat a pigeon a day.
6. Help the police,	o	o f) … fail your exams now.
7. I've half a mind to join the National Front.	o	o g) … he thought he was a painter.
8. If this machine is out of order, see the landlord.	o	o h) I'm married, I do both.
9. It begins when you sink in his arms,	o	o i) If so, it must have been a stupid questic
10. Keep London tidy,	o	o j) If it's in order, see the waitress.
11. Make love, not war.	o	o k) Make sure it doesn't pay.
12. My inferiority complexes	o	o l) So I did, and it was.
13. Nationalise crime.	o	o m) That's all I'll need.
14. Smile, they said, life could be worse.	o	o n) The other 20% pay for it.
15. The Labour Party is the answer!	o	o o) What do the other two do with it?

Task 2) *Unjumble the words in brackets to complete the sentences.*

1. As I *said before, I never repeat myself* _____.
   (before, – I – myself. – never – repeat – said)

2. Everyone has _____.
   (a – don't – film. – have – just – memory, – photographic – some)

3. He got lost _____.
   (and – in – it – was – territory. – thought – unfamiliar)

4. I've had _____.
   (amnesia – maybe – once – twice.)

5. Marriage _____.
   (a – a – is – it's – not – sentence. – word,)

6. There are three _____.
   (and – can – can't. – count – kinds – of – people: – those – those- who – who)

7. (Time is _____.
   (a – a – beautician. – but – great – healer – terrible)

8. Welcome _____.
   (and – back – set – to – twenty – Utah – watch – years. – your)

© Ernst Klett Sprachen GmbH, Stuttgart 2011
Photocopiable
ISBN 978-3-12-534645-1

ɔlʒ Klett

One-Liners II

Task 1) *Unjumble the sentences a) – i) in the right-hand box. Which of the starters 1. – 9. do they go with?*

1. A clear conscience...   o————————o   a) *is usually the sign of a bad memory*   .
                                            (a – bad – is – memory – of – sign – the – usually)

2. Always go to ...   o   o   b) _____ .
                                            (a – except – from – inevitable – machine – vending)

3. As long ...   o   o   c) _____ .
                                            (amnesia – as – can – had – I – I've – remember)

4. Be nice to ...   o   o   d) _____ .
                                            (and – believed – gullible – I – I – them – was)

5. Change is ...   o   o   e) _____ .
                                            (and – get – hungry – naked – then – things – wet – worse)

6. Hard work ...   o   o   f) _____ ?
                                            (anyone – but – chance – it – killed – never – why)

7. I don't have ...   o   o   g) _____ .
                                            (a – but – do – find – I – interesting – problem – solution – the)

8. They told me ...   o   o   h) _____ .
                                            (because – choose – home – kids – nursing – they'll – your – your)

9. We are born ...   o   o   i) _____ .
                                            (funerals – go – or – other – people's – they – to – won't – yours)

Task 2) *Find the missing words to complete the graffiti. Write the answers on a separate piece of paper.*

1. Bigamy: one wife too many. – **Mo...**: same thing.
2. Wanted: **Tele...** You know where to apply.
3. I bet you I could stop **ga...**
4. I couldn't care less about **ap...**
5. I'd give my right arm to be **am...**
6. Losing a husband can be hard, in my case it was almost **im...**
7. Save a **t...** Eat a beaver.
8. **Va...** begins when Dad says, "I know a short cut."
9. **Cla...** meeting cancelled due to unforeseen events.
10. Never answer an **an...** letter.
11. Borrow money from a **pe...** – they don't expect it back.
12. Twelve out of ten people cannot understand **ma...**
13. I have a strong will but a weak **w...**
14. Not all men are fools – some are **ba...**
15. Lord, if I can't be skinny, please let all my friends be **f...**

 © Ernst Klett Sprachen GmbH, Stuttgart 2011
Photocopiable
ISBN 978-3-12-534645-1

Rhyming Slang

Task 1) *Draw lines from the phrases to the correct parts of the man's body and his clothes.*

1. Barnet (Fair) o

2. Dicky (Dirt) o

3. Round the Houses o

4. Sky rocket o

5. Tit for (tat) o

6. Whistle (and Flute) o

- o a) Darby Kelly
- o b) German Band
- o c) Ham and Eggs
- o d) Hampstead Heath
- o e) I Suppose
- o f) Loaf of Bread
- o g) Minced Pies
- o h) North And South
- o i) Plates of Meat
- o j) Queen Mum

Task 2) *Try to guess the meaning of the rhyming slang words in the following sentences.*

1. Fancy a cup of **Rosie Lee**? – *Tea* _____

2. He can't hear a thing you say. He's **Mutt and Jeff**! – _____

3. I couldn't **Adam and Eve** it! – _____

4. I've just bought myself a new **jam jar**. – _____

5. Let me have a **butcher's (hook)**! – _____

6. Let's go down to the **rub-a-dub** for a pint or two. – _____

7. My mother-in-law always has a bottle of **Mother's Ruin** in the cupboard. – _____

8. My wife's gone and left me on my **Tod (Sloane)**. – _____

9. There was a right **pen and ink** in the kitchen. – _____

10. What's wrong with your husband? He hasn't said a **Dicky (bird)** for hours. – _____

11. You can't believe what he says. He's always telling **porkies (pork pies)**. – _____

12. My mother-in-law she does **rabbit (and pork)** on a bit. You can't get a word in edgeways! – _____

© Ernst Klett Sprachen GmbH, Stuttgart 2011
Photocopiable
ISBN 978-3-12-534645-1

Klett

Bingo

Task 1) *Match the numbers.*

1. Bull's eye	1
2. Clickety click	10
3. Downing Street	11
4. Kelly's eye	14
5. Key of the door	18
6. Legs	22
7. Old age pension	50
8. The Beatles number	52
9. The same both ways	64
10. Top of the house	65
11. Two fat ladies	66
12. Two little ducks	69
13. Valentine's Day	88
14. Weeks in a year	90

Task 2) *What numbers are these?*

1. A Duck And A Flea – 23

2. A Flea In Heaven – _____

3. All The Beans – _____

4. Blind – _____

5. Chopsticks – _____

6. Doctor's Orders – _____

7. Fat lady with a duck – _____

8. Goodbye Teens – _____

9. Half A Crown – _____

10. Halfway House – _____

11. Lucky – _____

12. Nearly there – _____

13. One Fat Lady – _____

14. One Little Duck – _____

15. One Little Flea – _____

16. Rugby Team – _____

17. Seven dozen – _____

18. Sunset Strip – _____

19. Sweet – _____

20. Three Score And Ten – _____

21. Two Little Fleas – _____

22. Baker's Dozen – _____

Task 3) *Have a game of bingo using these names.*

© Ernst Klett Sprachen GmbH, Stuttgart 2011
Photocopiable
ISBN 978-3-12-534645-1

Newspapers and Newsletters

Newspaper Headlines

Headlines can almost be considered an art form in British newspapers. Popular newspapers such as *The Sun*, *The Mail*, etc. pride themselves on their eye-catching headlines, which can be both amusing and aggressively critical. *The Sun* in particular is well-known for its sports headlines, one famous example being "SWEDES 1, TURNIPS 0" when the English football team, referred to by the derogatory name "turnips", lost to the Swedish team (Swedes) in an international qualifying game some years ago, and was also heavily criticized for the headline "GOTCHA!", when the British Navy sunk an Argentinean battleship in the Falklands War in 1983.

Headlines are mostly elliptical in nature and as a result can be very ambiguous, such ambiguities often produce an amusing effect.

The basic principles are: <u>ellipsis</u> due to articles, auxiliaries, etc. being omitted; <u>ambiguities</u> due to one or more words having more than one meaning, and sometimes the same word can be a different part of speech (noun, verb, etc).; <u>ambiguities</u> due to two words suggesting a different or unexpected context; <u>wrong word order</u>.

Copymaster I: Task 1 is concerned with headlines which include ambiguous words creating an amusing effect. Explain the principle (cf. above) in the first headline and explain the two meanings of "hit". Form small groups and ask them to find the ambiguity in the second example. Provide clues if necessary. Allow the groups to use dictionaries as needed. Then let the groups work on the remaining examples by themselves. Monitor the groups' progress and check the solutions together with the whole class. Task 2 consists of headlines where the ambiguity not only produces a humorous effect but also leads to possible misunderstandings. The task is therefore to speculate on what the article might have been about. After dealing with the first example together with the whole class, ask groups to work on the remaining headlines. It is recommended to initially check their answers after each example to make sure that they are proceeding in the right way. When checking on answers it is probably a good idea to ask the groups to justify their answers. With high-level groups the task could become a writing activity: "Write a short article to go with the text."

Copymaster II: In this Task 1 the learners are required to make a clear and unambiguous sentence from each of the headlines. After working on the first headline together with the whole class to show the principle (cf. above) and to demonstrate how to solve the task, ask the groups to work on the other headlines one by one.

Short News Reports

Because of their compactness, the articles on this page, all of which have been taken from English-language newspapers, contain a number of humorous ambiguities.

Copymaster I: The task on this sheet is to find and underline the various ambiguities that produce amusing effects in the texts. After doing the first example together with the whole class, let groups work on the rest of the short articles one by one. Dictionaries should be allowed. When reporting, the groups should not only say which words they have underlined but also explain the ambiguity.

Copymaster II: The articles on this page contain both mistakes in language and mistakes in reference. The task is to improve the sentence either by correcting the mistake, re-sequencing the words or by completing or re-writing the article. Do the first article together with the whole class as an example before letting the groups do the following articles one by one. Check and compare the articles that the groups read out. Dictionaries can be used.

Church News

The articles in this section are all taken from local church magazines and mostly concern news and information for the local congregation. They have been mainly written by volunteers unused to writing texts for magazines rather than by professional journalists, and therefore may often contain mistakes, ambiguities etc., often with hilarious effect.

Copymaster I: In this task the learners are required to discover the cause of the ambiguity and to underline the corresponding part of the text, after which the task is then to correct and re-write the text. Go through the first example together with the class to illustrate the correct procedure. Then ask the learners to work in groups. The groups can use dictionaries if they wish. After each article ask the groups to read out their version for checking and comparing.

Copymaster II: In this task the learners are asked to re-write the texts to remove the ambiguities. This can be done in the same way as with Copymaster I. Finally the learners are asked to review the sentences in both this task and in the previous task in Copymaster I and decide which of the original texts they like best or found most amusing. This can be done either in an open class discussion, or by having a vote, where each learner writes down her/his favourite three and the votes are counted on the board.

Small Ads

Many people try to save money when preparing small ads, and make the text as short as possible. Due to the consequent compact style, there is often the risk of producing an unintended humorous effect due to spelling mistakes, wrong or imprecise words, wrong reference due to ellipsis, etc.

Copymaster I: In the task the learners are asked to correct and re-write the ads. Ask the class to look at the first ad to find the mistake and then let them re-write it in small groups. Check by asking the groups to read out their versions before letting the groups work on the remaining ads.

Copymaster II: Here the task is to find the errors and ambiguities in the ads. Depending on the time available, the groups can be given either 4-6 or all of the examples to work on. They should not only explain what is wrong, but where necessary correct the ads.

Refer to Page 6 for basic ways of working with the copymasters.

Headlines I

Task 1) *Why are the following headlines ambiguous and amusing? Underline and correct the ambiguous words.*

① PASSENGERS HIT BY CANCELLED TRAINS

② THREE BATTERED IN FISH SHOP

③ STRIP CLUB SHOCK – MAGISTRATES MAY ACT ON INDECENT SHOWS

④ BBQ OF SENIOR CITIZENS A BIG SUCCESS – WILL BECOME AN ANNUAL EVENT

⑤ KIDS MAKE NUTRITIOUS SNACKS

⑥ POLICE FOUND SAFE UNDER BLANKET

⑦ REAGAN WINS ON BUDGET, BUT MORE LIES AHEAD

⑧ EX-ALDERMAN DIES – ONE OF EIGHT AXED BY TORIES

⑨ BANK DRIVE-IN WINDOW BLOCKED BY BOARD

⑩ STOLEN PAINTING FOUND BY TREE

Task 2) *What do you think the following articles were about?*

① DRUNK GETS NINE MONTHS IN VIOLIN CASE

② RED TAPE HOLDS UP NEW BRIDGE

③ 20-YEAR FRIENDSHIP ENDS AT THE ALTAR

④ MAN RECOVERING AFTER FATAL ACCIDENT

⑤ BRITISH LEFT WAFFLES ON FALKLAND ISLANDS

⑥ PROSTITUTES APPEAL TO POPE

⑦ PRISONERS ESCAPE AFTER EXECUTION

⑧ INCLUDE YOUR CHILDREN WHEN BAKING COOKIES

⑨ DEAD POLICEMAN IN THE FORCE FOR 18 YEARS

⑩ WOMAN KICKED BY HUSBAND SAID TO BE GREATLY IMPROVED

⑪ AUTOS KILLING 110 A DAY, LET'S RESOLVE TO DO BETTER

⑭ PROTESTOR TRIES TO SPOIL PLAY BUT THE ACTORS SUCCEEDED

⑫ TWO CONVICTS EVADE NOOSE, JURY HUNG

⑬ DEAF MUTE GETS NEW HEARING IN KILLING

© Ernst Klett Sprachen GmbH, Stuttgart 2011
Photocopiable
ISBN 978-3-12-534645-1

Klett

Headlines II

Task: *Make a clear and unambiguous sentence from each of the following headlines.*

1. MINERS REFUSE TO WORK AFTER DEATH

2. STEALS CLOCK, FACES TIME

3. IRAQI HEAD SEEKS ARMS

4. SURVIVOR OF SIAMESE TWINS JOINS PARENTS

5. 'LEONORE' ONLY OPERA BEETHOVEN WROTE ON MONDAY EVENING

6. FATHER OF TEN SHOT DEAD – MISTAKEN FOR RABBIT

7. QUARTER OF A MILLION CHINESE LIVE ON WATER

8. NJ JUDGE TO RULE ON NUDE BEACH

9. NEW VACCINE MAY CONTAIN AIDS

10. COUNCIL CLAIM STREET WAS DEMOLISHED BY ACCIDENT

11. TWO SISTERS REUNITED AFTER 18 YEARS IN CHECKOUT COUNTER

12. CRASH COURSES FOR PRIVATE PILOTS

1. _____

2. _____

3. _____

4. _____

5. _____

6. _____

7. _____

8. _____

9. _____

10. _____

11. _____

12. _____

© Ernst Klett Sprachen GmbH, Stuttgart 2011
Photocopiable
ISBN 978-3-12-534645-1

Short News Reports I

Task: *Underline the words and phrases that are ambiguous and so produce a humorous effect.*

① At a meeting to discuss the route of a proposed ring road, the highways committee chairman said: "We intend to take the road through the cemetery – provided we can get permission from the various <u>bodies</u> concerned."

② British Rail said it was hoped that from 8 a.m. today a normal service would run, with trains liable to delays of up to 20 minutes.

③ Dying is to cost more at King's Lynn, Norfolk. Higher burial charges are being introduced at cemeteries. The increased cost of living is blamed.

④ Our own bishop has promised to take the chair. There will be a very strong platform to support him.

⑤ Two men were shot, one in the foot and one in the leg, when police fired over rioters' heads in Londonderry. They were taken to hospital.

⑥ A new German play including scenes of full frontal nudity and love-making opens at Leeds Playhouse tonight. A spokesman for the theatre said: "It was not until the dress rehearsal that we realised there would be nude scenes in the play."

⑦ The vicar has reported an increased number of people attending church services this year. He also stated that death watch beetle had been confirmed in the church.

⑧ Decrying the growth of hippie communities on the outskirts of town, the mayor asserted: "Johnstown has managed to grow from a small settlement to a thriving town without the benefit of pot smoking, nudism and sexual intercourse, and there is no reason now why any of these things should be necessary now."

⑨ Princess Margaret's daring but very fashionable hat caused a sensation when she opened a school for the blind at Sevenoaks yesterday.

⑩ General practitioners were responsible for more than 80 percent of the hospital confinements of borough mothers.

⑪ Canadian typist Chamber Landis, 23, has often had her leg pulled about her unusual Christian name. But it will be worse now. She has just married Vancouver salesman Les Potts.

⑫ Jenkins, it is claimed, was driving at a high rate of speed and swerving from side to side. As he approached the crossing he started directly towards it and crashed into Miss Miller's rear end, which was sticking out into the road about a foot. Luckily she escaped injury, and the damage can easily be remedied with a new coat of paint.

© Ernst Klett Sprachen GmbH, Stuttgart 2011
Photocopiable
ISBN 978-3-12-534645-1

Klett

Short News Reports II

Task: *Improve the texts. Write your suggestions on a separate piece of paper.*

① In the event of a nuclear attack children will be given a day off school, says the Scottish Home and Health Department.

② The driver had a narrow escape as a broken board penetrated his cabin and just missed his head. This had to be removed before he could be released.

③ Blackburn Times reporter Valerie Seaton will not forget the night she danced with Prime Minister Edward Heath at a Young Conservative ball and ended up in the maternity ward of the local hospital.

④ Mr Goodman expressed his appreciation and said he did like to feel he could claim some little part in the development of the district. When he came the population had been 22,500 and now it was 33,000.

⑤ *Ghana is going to change over to driving on the right. The change will be made gradually.*

⑥ Wooden benches for the important soccer game next week have been replaced by club officials.

⑦ Ladies who have kindly offered to act as school crossing wardens are reminded that if they attempt to carry out their duties without their clothing on motorists are unlikely to take notice of them.

⑧ The local vicar thinks it is impossible for his parishioners – most of whom are boarding-house keepers – to keep all the Ten Commandments, so he has reduced them to nine for his services.

⑨ 'The lack of toilet facilities is absolutely disgraceful,' he said. The only solution was a major reconstruction of the House or a new Chamber.

⑫ A new golf club has opened in Kenia. If your ball lands on or near a crocodile you have the option of moving the ball half a club's length away – or moving the crocodile.

⑩ Winners in the home-made red wine section were Mrs. Davis (fruity, well-rounded), Mrs. Raynor (fine colour and full-bodied), and Miss Ogle-Smith (slightly acid, but should improve if laid down).

⑪ Letters were sent to 665 men. Each envelope was marked 'important' in large letters, so that those men who could not read might have the letters read to them.

⑬ The winner of the competition to guess the number of sweets in the jar was Mrs. Y who will therefore travel to Mallorca by air, spend five days in a luxury hotel (all inclusive) and fly home via Paris, without any need to spend a penny.

⑭ *Donald's father told the court that his son's personality had completely changed since the accident. His career in the catering industry was finished because of the accident and he still carried a chip on his shoulder.*

© Ernst Klett Sprachen GmbH, Stuttgart 2011
Photocopiable
ISBN 978-3-12-534645-1

Church News I

Task: *The following sentences are ambiguous. Underline the ambiguous words and phrases and rewrite the sentences on a separate piece of paper.*

1. Eight new choir robes are currently needed, due to the addition of several new members and to the deterioration of some older ones.

2. ANOINTING OF THE SICK If you are going to be hospitalized for an operation, contact the pastor. Special prayers also for those who are seriously sick by request.

3. Irving Benson and Jessie Carter were married on October 24 in the church. So ends a friendship that began in their school days.

4. Please place your donation in the envelope along with the deceased person you want remembered.

5. Remember in prayer the many who are sick of our church and community.

6. The concert held in Fellowship Hall was a great success. Special thanks are due to the minister's daughter, who laboured the whole evening at the piano, which as usual fell upon her.

7. There is a sign-up sheet for anyone wishing to be baptized on the table in the foyer.

8. A bean supper will be held on Tuesday evening in the Church Hall. Music will follow.

9. A new loudspeaker system has been installed in the church. It was given by one of our members in honour of his wife.

10. At the evening service tonight, the sermon topic will be "What is Hell?" - Come early and listen to our choir practice.

11. It's Drug Awareness Week: Get involved in drugs before your children do.

12. Janet Smith has volunteered to strip and refinish the communion table in the sanctuary.

13. Ladies, don't forget the rummage sale. It is a great chance to get rid of those things not worth keeping around the house. Don't forget your husbands.

14. Next Sunday, a special collection will be taken to defray the cost of the new carpet. All those wishing to do something on the new carpet will come forward and get a piece of paper.

15. Over the massive front doors of a church, these words were inscribed: The Gates of Heaven. Below that was a small cardboard sign which read: Please use other entrance.

16. The sermon this morning: CONTEMPORARY ISSUES #3 "EUTHANASIA" – The closing song: TAKE MY LIFE.

© Ernst Klett Sprachen GmbH, Stuttgart 2011
Photocopiable
ISBN 978-3-12-534645-1

Church News II

Task 1) *The following sentences are ambiguous. Re-write the sentences to make the meaning clear.*

EVENING AT 7 IN THE PARISH HALL
MON ALCOHOLICS ANONYMOUS
TUE ABUSED SPOUSES
WED EATING DISORDERS
THU SAY NO TO DRUGS
FRI TEEN SUICIDE WATCH
SAT SOUP KITCHEN
SUNDAY SERMON 9 A. M. "AMERICA'S JOYOUS FUTURE"

1. The eighth-graders will be presenting Shakespeare's Hamlet in the church basement on Friday at 7 p.m. The congregation is invited to attend this tragedy.

2. The Low Self Esteem Support Group will meet Thursday at 7 p.m. Please use the back door.

3. The 'Over 60s Choir' will be disbanded for the summer with the thanks of the entire church.

4. The rosebud on the altar this morning is to announce the birth of David Alan Belzer, the sin of Rev. and Mrs. Julius Belzer.

5. Weight Watchers will meet at 7 p.m. at the First Presbyterian Church. Please use the large double door at the side entrance.

6. This afternoon there will be a meeting in the south and north ends of the church. Children will be baptized at both ends.

7. This being Easter Sunday, we will ask Mrs. Lewis to come forward and lay an egg on the altar.

8. Thursday at 5pm there will be a meeting of the Little Mothers Club. All wishing to become Little Mothers, please see the minister in his private study.

9. Twenty-two members were present at the church meeting held at the home of Mrs. Marsha Crutchfield last evening. Mrs. Crutchfield and Mrs. Rankin sang a duet: The Lord Knows Why.

Task 2) *Which of the messages do you like best?*

 © Ernst Klett Sprachen GmbH, Stuttgart 2011
Photocopiable
ISBN 978-3-12-534645-1

Small Ads I

Task: *Correct the mistakes and ambiguities.*

1. **A superb** and inexpensive restaurant. Fine food expertly served by waitresses in appetizing forms.

2. **For Sale** – Eight puppies from a German Shepherd and an Alaskan Hussy.

3. **Wanted:** Chambermaid in rectory. Love in, $200 a month. References required.

4. **And now, the Superstore** – unequaled in size, unmatched in variety, unrivaled inconvenience.

5. **For Sale.** Three canaries of undermined sex.

6. **Have several** very old dresses from grandmother in beautiful condition.

7. **Creative daily specials**, including select offerings of beef, foul, fresh vegetables, salads, quiche.

8. **For sale:** an antique desk suitable for lady with thick legs and large drawers.

9. **Mixing bowl set** designed to please a cook with round bottom for efficient beating.

10. **For Rent:** 6-room hated apartment.

11. Get rid of aunts: Zap does the job in 24 hours.

12. **Mother's helper** – peasant working conditions.

1. _____.

2. _____.

3. _____.

4. _____.

5. _____.

6. _____.

7. _____.

8. _____.

9. _____.

10. _____.

11. _____.

12. _____.

© Ernst Klett Sprachen GmbH, Stuttgart 2011
Photocopiable
ISBN 978-3-12-534645-1

Small Ads II

Task: *What is wrong or ambiguous in the following adverts? Underline the word or phrase.*

1. **Christmas tag-sale**. Handmade gifts for the <u>hard-to-find</u> person.

2. **Dinner Special** – Turkey $2.35; Chicken or Beef $2.25; Children $2.00.

3. **Ladies and gentlemen**, now you can have a bikini for a ridiculous figure.

4. **Lost**: small apricot poodle. Reward. Neutered. Like one of the family.

5. **Man wanted** – to work in dynamite factory. Must be willing to travel.

6. **We do not** tear your clothing with machinery. We do it carefully by hand.

7. **Dog for sale**: eats anything and is fond of children.

8. **Illiterate?** – Write today for free help.

9. **Four-poster bed**, 101 years old. Perfect for antique lover.

10. **Man**, honest. Will take anything.

11. **Our bikinis are exciting.** They are simply the tops.

12. **Our tongue sandwiches** speak for themselves.

13. **See ladies blouses.** 50% off!

14. **Semi-Annual after-Christmas Sale**

15. **Stock up and save.** Limit: one.

16. **Tired** of cleaning yourself? Let me do it.

17. **Wanted:** Unmarried girls to pick fresh fruit and produce at night.

18. **Swim in the lovely hotel pool** while you drink it all in.

19. **Now is your chance** to have your ears pierced and get an extra pair to take home, too.

20. **Sheer stockings.** Designed for fancy dress, but so serviceable that lots of women wear nothing else.

21. **The hotel has** bowling alleys, tennis courts, comfortable beds, and other athletic facilities.

22. **Wanted:** Preparer of food. Must be dependable, like the food business, and be willing to get hands dirty.

23. **We will oil** your sewing machine and adjust tension in your home for $1.00.

24. **When you are thirsty**, try 7-UP, the refreshing drink in the green bottle with the big 7 on it and U-P after.

© Ernst Klett Sprachen GmbH, Stuttgart 2011
Photocopiable
ISBN 978-3-12-534645-1

Running Gags

Running gags are a literary device that takes the form of a joke or an amusing reference which is repeated again and again – sometimes in an adapted form – the repeats often increasing the humorous effect and becoming more humorous than the original joke.

Riddles

Riddles are question and answer jokes where the humour is based on puns using words that are spelt and/or sound alike. There are various formats, a number of which are shown on the three copymasters. As a result of the way the riddles play with words, they are a useful device for enhancing learners' language awareness and show how native speakers of English often play with words for humorous effect.

This section offers three copymasters, but normally they should be used only one at a time, unless the class asks to do more!

Copymaster I: The riddles in Task 1 are a variation of the spoonerisms shown in the section Classic Native-Speaker Mistakes and can also be used as a follow-up to the activities offered there, or alternatively these can be used as an introduction to the other spoonerism activities. With the help of the first example, explain the principle that the first letters or even syllables and whole words are exchanged and point out that the words may be spelt the same but sound differently or vice versa. Go through two or three of the riddles before asking small groups to work on the rest. Task 2 is a matching exercise based on puns. Do one or two (or if necessary more) to introduce the learners to the principle, before letting small groups work on the remaining examples. Monitor the groups as much as possible and check that everybody has understood.

Copymaster II: In Task 1 the learners have to find the correct answers as in Task 2 of Copymaster I. All the questions are based on food with a strong leaning towards cannibals and vampires – favourite topics for riddles. Task 2 introduces a new type of riddle: "What do you get if you cross … with a …?" The answers have to be matched with the questions. Using the first question as an example, point out to the class how the correct answers should always combine the two elements of the question. If necessary, try a second question before giving each group 2-3 to work on. The groups should then not only give the correct solution but explain why they think the suggested answer is correct.

Copymaster III: The running gag element in Task 1 is connected with elephants (another favourite topic for riddles). The puns are mostly based on similar sounding words and/or a kind of surrealist logic. Work through the task in the same way as in Task 2 of Copymaster II. There is no topic linking the examples in Task 2. The learners have to find the correct answer by looking for words that are linked to the context of the question. Explain the principle with the help of the first example, and then let the groups find as many as they can.

Waiter, Waiter

"Waiter, Waiter" jokes are running gags based on short conversations between a waiter and a customer. There are two variations: a two-part complaint dialogue, where the customer starts and the waiter gives a humorous response, and a three-part dialogue, where the customer provides the humorous response in the third part.

Copymaster I: In Task 1 the learners have to fill in the missing word. The first letter of each missing word has been given and it should be possible to guess the word from the context. With weaker groups, teachers can prompt by indicating which word in the customer's complaint provides the clue. After one or two examples, allow the groups to work by themselves. Task 2 is a matching exercise based on puns. This is an ideal activity for giving one part (waiter or customer) to each member of the group and asking them to find the person with the other half of the dialogue.

Copymaster II: Task 1 requires the learners to reconstruct the whole dialogue by matching up the three parts. After one example with the whole class, the remaining examples can be given to small groups, who then act out the dialogues.

Doctor, Doctor

"Doctor, Doctor" jokes work in the same way as "Waiter, Waiter" jokes. The patient starts by describing her/his problem, and the doctor gives a humorous response based on a pun.

Copymaster I: Here the learners have to find the correct word to complete the patient's description of her/his problem.

Copymaster II: In both tasks the learners have to find the correct word, in Task 1 in the doctor's response, in Task 2 in the patient's explanation. To help the learners, the first letter of the missing words has been given.

Knock, Knock

"Knock, knock" jokes are one of the best-known formats based on puns. It is a kind of role-play for two people/groups of people and consists of five lines:

1. The first person/group says: "Knock, knock!" to indicate they are standing outside wishing to enter the building.
2. The second person/group says "Who's there?".
3. The first person/group then responds with a name.
4. The second person/group repeats that response plus who?
5. The first person/group then produces the punch line, which normally involves a punnish misuse of the word or name used in the response Step 3.

Task 1 is just for acting out to get the learners used to the format before starting the more creative tasks.

Task 2 is a matching exercise based on lines 3-5 of the basic format. After doing the first example with the whole of the class, give each group two or three of the remaining examples, the task being to find the correct response. Divide the class

Refer to Page 6 for basic ways of working with the copymasters.

into groups, and the individual members of the group approach members of the other groups and start off the full five-step basic format. Task 3 offers mainly non-standard responses that can be dealt with in a similar way to Task 2. Finally Task 4 requires the learners to be creative and find their own responses to the words and phrases given. Help can be given if and when necessary.

I say! I say! I say!

"I say! I say! I say!" was the opening gambit used by stand-up comedians in the Victorian music hall to show when they wanted to start to tell a joke. It was a kind of signal to the audience "Listen to this!" to tell them that a joke – often a joke based on a (terrible) pun – was about to be told. All kinds of jokes were introduced in this way. The ones used on this copymaster are puns based on the names of towns and countries. The format is: Person A: mentions a relative or relatives who have travelled somewhere abroad. Person B: suggests a place in the area mentioned. Person A then responds with a statement that includes a pun based on the name of the place suggested.

The two tasks are matching exercises which produce similar three-part dialogues. Do the first example of Task 1 with the whole class. Prompt for the first match by asking the class for a place in the middle column that they connect with the area mentioned in the initial statement. When they have found the correct place, ask the class to try to say that place name in a different way suggesting one of the responses in the third column. If necessary, do a second example with the class before letting small groups try the remaining examples one by one. When they have completed Task 1, ask the groups to try and make similar three-part dialogues with the information provided in Task 2. Monitor the group work to avoid possible frustration.

Riddles I

Task 1) *"What's the difference between …?" Fill in the gaps.*

1. … a blind man and a sailor in jail? – One can't see to go; the other can't *go to sea*_____.

2. … a bus driver and a cold? – One knows the stops, the other stops the _____.

3. … a coyote and a flea? – One howls on the prairie, the other prowls on the _____.

4. … a garden sprinkler and a washerwoman? – One keeps the lawn wet, the other keeps the _____.

5. … a mirror and a gossip? – One _____ without _____, the other speaks without reflection.

6. … a man bitten by a mosquito and a man going on holiday? – One is _____ _____

   _____, the other is itching to go.

7. … a photocopying machine and a flu epidemic? – One makes facsimiles, the other makes sick _____.

8. … a squeeze and a louse? One is a bear hug, the other a _____.

9. … a thief and church bells? One _____ _____ _____, the other peals from the steeple.

10. … a train and a tree? One _____ _____ _____, the other sheds its leaves.

11. … an empty beer can and an idiot from Amsterdam? One is a hollow cylinder, the other a

    silly _____.

12. … pack-ice and a clothes brush? One crushes boats, the other _____ _____.

Task 2) *Match up the two parts of the following riddles.*

1. How does the Pope fly? o	o a) A Chinese football team.
2. What do you get if you dial 666? o	o b) A hippie-potamus.
3. What's 300 metres tall, weighs 7,620 tonnes and attracts bees? o	o c) A Moo Yorker.
	o d) An Eski-moo.
4. What's a hippie? o	o e) Fry-day.
5. What's an American cow called? o	o f) Jungle Bells.
6. What's an army? o	o g) Tarzan Stripes Forever.
7. What's an Eskimo cow called? o	o h) The Eiffel Flower.
8. What's got long hair and weighs about two tonnes? o	o i) The Australian police.
9. What's Tarzan's favourite carol? o	o j) The thing your leggies hang down from.
10. What's the best day to cook bacon and eggs? o	o k) The thingy up your sleevy.
11. What's the national anthem of the jungle? o	o l) With a holy-copter.
12. What's yellow, has twenty-two legs and two wings? o	

© Ernst Klett Sprachen GmbH, Stuttgart 2011
Photocopiable
ISBN 978-3-12-534645-1

Riddles II

Task 1) *Which answer goes with each of the riddles 1 – 12?*

1. What did the cannibal say when he saw a sleeping missionary? o
2. What do cannibals eat at parties? o
3. What's a cannibal who has eaten his mother's sister? o
4. What's a computer's favourite food? . o
5. What's a vampire's favourite fruit? o
6. What's a vampire's second favourite fruit? o
7. What's a vegetarian cannibal's favourite food? o
8. What's crunchy and lives in the Middle East? o
9. What liquid and comes out of the bottle at 100 miles an hour? o
10. What's made of dough, is 50 metres high and is not straight? o
11. What's sweet and swings from tree to tree? o
12. What's the highlight of a cannibal wedding? o

o a) A blood orange.
o b) A nectarine.
o c) An Aston Martini.
o d) An aunt-eater.
o e) Buttered host.
o f) 'Oh look! Breakfast in bed!'
o g) Silicon chips.
o h) Sultan vinegar crisps.
o i) Swedes.
o j) Tarzipan!
o k) The Leaning Tower of Pizza.
o l) Toasting the happy couple.

Task 2) *"What do you get if you cross ...?" Match the answers a) – o).*

1. a bee with 500 grams of mince beef? o
2. a chicken with gunpowder? o
3. a cow with an octopus? o
4. a crocodile with a camera? o
5. a famous detective with a bubble bath? o
6. a germ with a comedian? o
7. a hamburger with a Scotsman? o
8. a kangaroo with a sheep? o
9. a parrot with a homing pigeon? o
10. a pop-singer with a seat? o
11. a skunk with a boomerang? o
12. a woodwind instrument with an ancient Briton? o
13. a flea with a rabbit? o
14. an elephant with a fish? o
15. an MP3 player with a fridge? o

o a) A big Mac.
o b) A bird that can ask the way if it gets lost.
o c) A cow that milks itself.
o d) A horrible smell you can't get rid of.
o e) A rocking chair.
o f) A snap shot.
o g) A woolly jumper.
o h) An anglo-saxophone.
o i) An eggs-plosion.
o j) Humburgers.
o k) Sherlock Foams.
o l) Sick jokes.
o m) Cool music.
o n) Bugs Bunny.
o o) A pair of swimming trunks.

© Ernst Klett Sprachen GmbH, Stuttgart 2011
Photocopiable
ISBN 978-3-12-534645-1

Riddles III

Task 1) *Write the correct answers in the spaces provided.*

1. How do you get five elephants in a Mini? *Two in the front, two in the back and one in the glove compartment.*

2. What do elephants use to talk to each other? _____.

3. What time is it when an elephant sits on your car? _____.

4. What weighs four tonnes, has a trunk and is bright red? _____.

5. What's grey, has a trunk and takes off from Heathrow? _____.

6. What's grey, weighs four tonnes and leaves footprints in the butter? _____.

7. What's grey, weighs four tonnes and lives in California? _____.

8. What's grey, weighs four tonnes and wears glass slippers? _____.

9. What's the difference between an elephant and spaghetti? _____.

10. Why did the elephant leave the circus? _____.

a) A jumbo jet.
b) An elephant in the fridge.
c) An L.A. Phant.
d) Elephones.
e) Time to get a new one.
f) Elephants don't slip off your fork.
g) An embarrassed elephant.
h) Cinderelephant.
i) It was fed up of working for peanuts.
j) ~~Two in the front, two in the back and one in the glove compartment.~~

Task 2) *What did they say? Match questions and answers.*

1. What did Adam say to his wife on 24th December? o
2. What did Cinderella say when her holiday photos were not delivered on time? o
3. What did the big chimney say to the little chimney? o
4. What did the bus conductor say to the one-legged passenger? o
5. What did the cashier say to the adding machine? o
6. What did the frankfurter say to the ketchup? o
7. What did the North wind say to the South wind? o
8. What did the one ear say to the other ear? o
9. What did the rose say to the bee? o
10. What did the one strawberry say to the other strawberry? o

o a) "Between you and me we need a haircut."
o b) "Buzz off!"
o c) "Hop on!"
o d) "How about a game of draughts?"
o e) "I'm counting on you."
o f) "If we hadn't been in the same bed together, we wouldn't be in this jam."
o g) "It's Christmas, Eve."
o h) "One day my prints will come."
o i) "That's enough of your sauce."
o j) "You're far too young to smoke."

© Ernst Klett Sprachen GmbH, Stuttgart 2011
Photocopiable
ISBN 978-3-12-534645-1

Don't panic, sir, the spider on your bread will get it.

Waiter, Waiter I

Waiter, waiter! There's a fly in my soup.

Task 1) *Fill in the missing words.*

1. Waiter, there's a dead fly in my soup!   – Yes sir, it's the h*eat*_____ *which*_____ kills them.

2. Waiter, there's a dead fly in my soup!   – What do you expect for 50p - a l_____ one?

3. Waiter, there's a fly in my soup!   – It's OK, sir, there's no e_____ c_____.

4. Waiter, what's this fly doing in my soup?   – Um, looks like the b_____, sir.

5. Waiter, waiter, there's a bee in my soup.   – Yes, sir, it's the fly's d_____ o_____.

6. Waiter, there's a f_____ in my soup!   – OK ,sir, I'll tell him to hop it.

7. Waiter, there's a dead beetle in my soup.   – Yes sir, they're not very good s_____.

8. Waiter, there's a small slug on my salad.   – Just a minute, sir. I'll get you a l_____ one.

9. Waiter! Waiter! I can't eat this food! Bring me the m_____!   – But you can't eat him either, sir.

10. Waiter, there's something wrong with this egg you brought me.   – Nothing to do with me, sir. I only l_____ the table.

Task 2) *Match up the sentences.*

1. Waiter, waiter, will the pancakes be long? o

2. Waiter! There's no chicken in the chicken soup! o

3. Waiter, there's a worm on my plate. o

4. Watch out! Your thumb's in my soup! o

5. Waiter, how long will my sausages be? o

6. Waiter, my plate's wet! o

7. Waiter, waiter, is this a hair in my soup? o

8. Waiter, waiter, there's a twig in my soup. o

9. Waiter, waiter, there's a crocodile in my soup. o

10. Waiter, have you got soup on the menu? o

o   a) Don't worry, sir, it's not that hot!

o   b) Hold on, sir. I'll get the branch manager.

o   c) No, I wiped it this morning, sir.

o   d) No, sir - that's the soup!

o   e) Oh, about three or four inches if you're lucky.

o   f) Right, sir. There's no horse in the horseradish either!

o   g) That's your sausage, sir.

o   h) Well, sir, you told me to make it snappy!

o   i) Why, of course, sir. That's rabbit stew!

o   j) No, sir, round.

© Ernst Klett Sprachen GmbH, Stuttgart 2011
Photocopiable
ISBN 978-3-12-534645-1

Klett

Waiter, Waiter II

Task: *Take one part from each column to make waiter jokes.*

1. Waiter, bring me a fried egg with finger-marks in it, some lukewarm greasy chips and a portion of watery cabbage. o

2. Waiter, how long have you been here? o

3. Waiter, I can't eat this! o

4. Waiter, I'll have my bill now. o

5. Waiter, I'll have the pie, please. o

6. Waiter, my bill please. o

7. Waiter, this lobster's only got one claw. o

8. Waiter, waiter, have you got frog's legs? o

9. Waiter, what do you call this? o

10. Waiter, what is this stuff? o

11. Waiter, bring me a hot dog. o

12. Waiter, would you close the window, please? o

i. Yes, sir. With pleasure.

ii. Yes sir!

iii. Why, is it draughty?

iv. Why not, sir?

v. We don't do food like that, sir!

vi. That's bean salad, sir.

vii. Six months, sir.

viii. I expect he's been in a fight, sir.

ix. How did you find your steak, sir?

x. How did you find your luncheon, sir?

xi. Cottage pie, sir.

xii. Anything with it, sir?

o a) You haven't given me a knife and fork.

o b) You did yesterday.

o c) Yes, it's blown the steak off my plate three times.

o d) With a magnifying glass.

o e) Well, I've just bitten on a piece of the door.

o f) Well, bring me the winner!

o g) Well, hop over here with a menu.

o h) Oh, I just moved the potato and there it was.

o i) No, with mustard.

o j) If it's anything like last time, I'd better have a hammer and chisel.

o k) I don't want to know its life story. What is it now?

o l) Ah, then it can't be you who took my order.

 Klett

© Ernst Klett Sprachen GmbH, Stuttgart 2011
Photocopiable
ISBN 978-3-12-534645-1

Doctor, Doctor I

Task: *Fill in the gaps with the correct words from the box.*

dustbin	glasses	horses	bug	invisible	liver
pack of cards	~~pen~~	pencil	roll of film	shoplifting	bell

DOCTOR, DOCTOR, I THINK I NEED GLASSES!

YES. I COULD TELL THE MOMENT YOU WALKED THROUGH THE WINDOW.

1. Patient: Doctor, Doctor I've just swallowed a _pen_____.
   Doctor: Well sit down and write your name!

2. Patient: Doctor, Doctor, I keep dreaming about _____!
   Doctor: Are they nightmares?

3. Patient: Doctor, Doctor, I think I need _____!
   Doctor: Yes. I could tell the moment you walked through the window.

4. *Patient: Doctor, Doctor, my boy has swallowed my pen! What shall I do?*

   Doctor: Use a _____ until I get there.

5. Patient: Doctor, Doctor, I feel like a _____.
   Doctor: Sit down and I'll deal with you later.

6. Patient: Doctor, Doctor! My small son has just swallowed a _____.
   Doctor: Don't worry. Let him rest a bit and we'll see what develops.

7. **Patient: Doctor, Doctor, have you got anything for my _____?**
   Doctor: What about some onions?

8. *Patient: Doctor, doctor! Nobody notices me, I feel _____.*
   Doctor: I'm sorry, I can't see you now.

9. Patient: Doctor! Doctor! I think I'm turning into a _____.
   Doctor: Rubbish!

10. Patient: Doctor! Doctor! I can't stop myself _____!
    Doctor: Take two of these pills. If that does not work, bring me a CD player.

11. Patient: Doctor, Doctor, I keep seeing an insect flying around the room!

    Doctor: Don't worry. It's just a _____ going around.

12. Patient: Doctor, Doctor, I feel like a _____.
    Doctor: Don't worry, take these pills and if it doesn't get better, give me a ring tomorrow.

© Ernst Klett Sprachen GmbH, Stuttgart 2011
Photocopiable
ISBN 978-3-12-534645-1

Doctor, Doctor II

Task 1)   *What does the doctor say?*

Patient

1. Doctor, Doctor, will I be able to do the tango after the operation?

2. Doctor, Doctor, nobody takes me seriously.

3. Doctor, Doctor, I feel like a light bulb!

4. Doctor, Doctor, I snore so loud I keep myself awake.

5. Doctor, Doctor, I've swallowed a spoon.

6. Doctor, Doctor, I keep thinking I'm a vampire.

7. Doctor, Doctor, I feel like a pair of curtains.

8. Doctor, Doctor, I keep getting smaller!

9. Doctor, Doctor, I feel like a piano.

10. Doctor, Doctor! I think I'm going to die.

Doctor

– No, you'll have to wait until you *get* h*ome* .

– That can't be t_____!

– Whatever t_____ you on!

– Sleep in a_____ r_____ then.

– Sit down and don't s_____.

– N_____, please.

– P_____ yourself together.

– I'm afraid you'll have to be a l_____ p_____.

– In that case I'd better take some n_____.

– That's the l_____ th_____ you'll do.

Task 2)   *What does the patient say?*

Patient

1. Doctor, Doctor, I keep s*tealing* things.

2. Doctor, Doctor, everyone calls me a l _____.

3. Doctor, Doctor, I need g_____.

4. Doctor, Doctor, I'm suffering from s_____.

5. Doctor, Doctor, I'd like a s_____ o_____.

6. Doctor, Doctor, I've a s _____ growing in my nose.

7. Doctor, Doctor, I feel like a d_____.

8. Doctor, Doctor, I think I'm in_____.

9. Doctor, Doctor, people keep ig_____ me.

10. Doctor, Doctor, I'm suffering from in_____.

Doctor

– Have you taken anything for it?

– Come, now, I don't believe that.

– You certainly do, sir. This is a fish and chip shop!

– One at a time please.

– Of course, come back tomorrow!

– I'll give you some cream for it.

– Sit!!

– Who said that?!?!?

– Next, please.

– Don't lose any sleep over it.

© Ernst Klett Sprachen GmbH, Stuttgart 2011
Photocopiable
ISBN 978-3-12-534645-1

Knock, Knock

Task 1) Act out the following three "Knock, Knock" jokes.

Knock, knock,	Knock, knock,	Knock, knock,
Who's there?	Who's there?	Who's there?
Ken.	Wayne.	Howard.
Ken who?	Wayne who?	Howard who?
Ken I come in, please?	Wayne you gonna open the door?	Howard you expect to find out, if you don't open up?

Task 2) Write down the final line of the following "Knock, Knock" jokes.

1. Wanda *let me in? It's freezing out here* _____.
2. Isabel _____
3. (Ewan) _____
4. Tennis _____
5. (Minnie) _____
6. Zippy _____
7. (Ida) _____
8. Toby _____
9. Ella Mann _____
10. Hugo _____
11. Hannah _____
12. Police _____

a) broken, or what?

b) first, I'm afraid!

c) It's not ...., it's Idaho!

d) let me in.

e) ~~let me in? It's freezing out here.~~

f) Mrs

g) tree, my dear Watson.

h) No not .... – Minnehaha!

i) No, just me.

j) or not to be!

k) partridge in a pear tree.

l) see.

Task 3) Match the following halves.

1. Old lady o
2. Kenya o
3. Repeat o
4. Twit o
5. Sal o
6. Shelby o
7. Yah o
8. Cowgo o
9. Hatch o
10. Ivan o
11. Harmony o
12. An author o

o a) … awful headache after all these stupid Knock, Knock jokes!

o b) Calm down, you idiot!

o c) … think of anything that's more fun than Knock, Knock jokes?

o d) … coming round the mountains when she comes.

o e) Bless you.

o f) … more of these terrible Knock Knock jokes?

o g) I didn't know you could yodel.

o h) No, Cow go MOO!!

o i) Not …… Knock Knock joke?

o j) … ong way to Tipperary …

o k) Who! Who! Who!

o l) You got an owl in there?

Task 4) Make Knock Knock jokes with the following names.

1. Sofa	4. Olive	7. Kay	10. Hawaii
2. Lettuce	5. Hammond	8. Datsun	11. Mary
3. Cook	6. Luke	9. Tank	12. Four eggs

© Ernst Klett Sprachen GmbH, Stuttgart 2011
Photocopiable
ISBN 978-3-12-534645-1

Klett

I say! I say! I say!

Task 1) *Make three part dialogues with examples from each of the three columns.*

1. My daughter's gone to the botanical gardens in London. ○
2. My mother-in-law has gone to St Petersburg. ○
3. My son's gone on a singing tour of South Korea. ○
4. My son's parents are from Croatia. ○
5. My wife went to a very bad concert out East. ○
6. My wife's gone mad in Venezuela. ○
7. My wife's gone to Northern Italy. ○
8. My wife's gone to the Welsh border. ○

i. Caracas? ○
ii. Genoa? ○
iii. Is she Russian? ○
iv. Kew? ○
v. Seoul? ○
vi. Singapore? ○
vii. Split? ○
viii. Wye? ○

a) I should think so. We've been married for 20 years. ○
b) No idea! ○
c) No, R&B. ○
d) No, she's taking her time. ○
e) No, they're still happily married. ○
f) Terrible. And the rest of the band were rubbish too. ○
g) Yes, absolutely mad! ○
h) Yes, it was full. ○

Task 2) *Now try these.*

1. My daughter went on a sailing course in Poole. ○
2. My father-in-law had an accident in Slovenia. ○
3. My wife caught a cold in the Gulf. ○
4. My wife smoked a joint near Manchester. ○
5. My wife's gone to Malaysia. ○
6. My wife's gone to the Indian coast. ○
7. My wife's had an accident on a volcano. ○
8. My wife's had an upset tummy in Laos. ○

i. Bled? ○
ii. Goa? ○
iii. In Dorset? ○
iv. In Hale? ○
v. Inkhazi? ○
vi. Krakatoa? ○
vii. Longkawi? ○
viii. Qatar? ○

a) Absolutely, I can't stop her! ○
b) Yes, she'd recommend it to anyone. ○
c) No. She broke her leg. ○
d) Like a stuck pig. ○
e) Yes, she was coughing for weeks. ○
f) Yes, constantly. ○
g) Yes, about 5000 miles. ○
h) No, she just blew it out again. ○

© Ernst Klett Sprachen GmbH, Stuttgart 2011
Photocopiable
ISBN 978-3-12-534645-1

Signs and Instructions

This chapter contains a wide selection of signs, instructions, warnings, etc. as well as the names of people, professions and places. All examples are amusing in some way – sometimes intentionally and sometimes unintentionally. Some of the examples have been made by native speakers, others by speakers of other languages.

English Signs

Copymaster I: Task 1 is a matching exercise where the learners have to say where they think the signs were found. The groups should not only match up sign and place, but also explain which words in the sign are deliberately ambiguous and give away the correct answer. Similarly, in Task 2, the class have to say which of the words in the sign have two meanings and so produce a humorous effect.

Copymaster II: Task 1 requires the learners to read through the various signs and decide which they like best and why. This could take the form of a discussion where every learner in the class chooses a sign and explains the reason for his or her choice. In Task 2 the learners have to find the mistakes in the signs, all of which were written by native speakers of English, and decide which of the mistakes were deliberate. It is impossible to say with certainty which were actually intended and which not, but in most if not all cases the errors were probably not deliberate. And asking the learners to decide is a very effective way of getting them to read intensively. For this reason the answer should not be given until after the activity has been completed. It is also quite often amusing for learners of English to see that native speakers are not always perfect!

International Tourism Signs

All these examples in this section have been found in hotels, restaurants and a variety of shops and buildings. The errors are mostly errors of translation either as a result of wrong use of dictionaries or by using one of the automatic translation services available online.

Copymaster I – Hotels: In Task 1 the learners have to work out what the signs are intended to mean and then put the sign into correct English. In Task 2 the signs are less clear and require a certain degree of speculation and discussion. This can be done by the whole class or in small groups. Having decided what they think the signs are supposed to mean, the groups can then produce a corrected version.

Copymaster II – Restaurants and Shops: Task 1 is very similar to the previous copymaster, but the signs are all from restaurants and menus. The same procedure can be adopted. Task 2 contains a number of signs from all types of shops and buildings. This activity can be done in groups, who not only have to produce an answer but also justify their answer with reference to the text.

Church Signs

In English-speaking countries, especially the United States and the UK, it is quite usual to find signs expressing religious messages in front of churches. These are very often formulated in an amusing way by use of deliberate ambiguity, etc.

Copymaster I: Task 1 is a fill-in exercise, the words in brackets having to be inserted in the right place to complete the sign. Task 2 requires the learners to reproduce the signs by unjumbling the words. In both tasks, do one example with the whole class, and then let small groups work out the rest of the signs.

Copymaster II: The church signs in Task 1 contain deliberate ambiguities for humorous effect. The learners have to underline the words with double meaning in each of the signs. They should also explain what the double meanings are. Task 2 requires the learners to go through all the signs in Task 1 (and those on Copymaster I) again and choose the sign they like best and think is most effective in attracting people's attention and expressing the church's message. This can be done in the form of a discussion in which each learner tells the whole group which sign he or she has chosen and why. The other members of the group then agree or disagree accordingly. This can be done with the whole class or in groups.

Warnings

Due to sometimes excessively strict official health and safety requirements and/or for reasons of political correctness, a number of everyday products have warnings printed on the label that may in some cases seem to be without reason. Such warnings form the basis for Tasks 1 and 2. Most if not all the examples used have actually been found on commercially available products.

Copymaster: Task 1 is a matching exercise requiring the learners to find the product on which the various warnings were found. The groups should not only provide an answer but also justify their answer. Task 2 requires the learners to think about the reasons why the various warnings were put on the product labels. In many cases this is due to law suits such as the famous court case against MacDonald's who were sued for damages because they served hot tea. This task can also take the form of a discussion in small groups and each group has to report to the whole class what conclusions they came to. If different groups produce different opinions, a class discussion can follow.

Names, Shops and Professions

This section looks at the way names can be used for humorous purposes using various kinds of ambiguities.

Copymaster I: Task 1 contains a list of internationally well-known people whose names betray the area in which they are famous. The task is to match the people with the descriptions offered. The names in Task 2 are real but the people are not famous, and the task is to speculate on the basis of their names what their occupation or profession might be. After dealing with the first name together with the whole class (asking for suggestions, collecting suggestions, perhaps asking the class to choose the best suggestion) the examples can be worked on in groups.

Refer to Page 6 for basic ways of working with the copymasters.

There is no obvious one single solution to any of the names, so any feasible suggestion should be accepted.

Copymaster II: Task 1 contains a list of shop names where there is a "punnish" connection between the name and what they sell. The class and/or groups make suggestions, give reasons and discuss what the best answer might be, if groups come up with different ideas. As virtually all the names have some reference to phrases and words used in real life in other contexts, Task 2 requires the groups to work out the origin of the names. Task 3 offers a list of real place names, most of which are in the UK. The task of guessing which places are in other countries is the preliminary to Task 4 which should provide a discussion on pleasant and unpleasant place names. Each member of the class makes a suggestion with reasons, the others agree or disagree offering their own preferences.

ATTENTION
DOG WALKERS
Pick up after your dogs.
Thank you.
DOGS
Grrrr, bark, woof.
Good dog.

THOU
SHALT
NOT
PARK
HERE

*NO SIGNS
ALLOWED*

PRESS UP TO GO UP
PRESS DOWN TO GO DOWN

English Signs I

Task 1) *Where do you think these signs were found?*

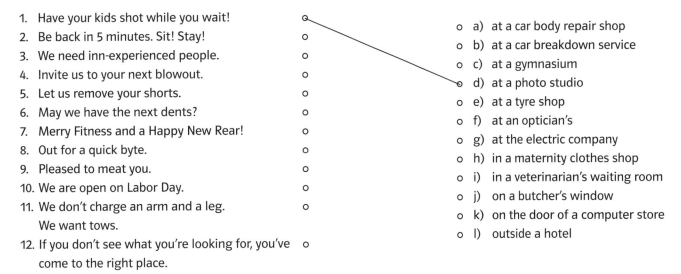

1. Have your kids shot while you wait!   o
2. Be back in 5 minutes. Sit! Stay!   o
3. We need inn-experienced people.   o
4. Invite us to your next blowout.   o
5. Let us remove your shorts.   o
6. May we have the next dents?   o
7. Merry Fitness and a Happy New Rear!   o
8. Out for a quick byte.   o
9. Pleased to meat you.   o
10. We are open on Labor Day.   o
11. We don't charge an arm and a leg.   o
    We want tows.
12. If you don't see what you're looking for, you've   o
    come to the right place.

- o a) at a car body repair shop
- o b) at a car breakdown service
- o c) at a gymnasium
- o d) at a photo studio
- o e) at a tyre shop
- o f) at an optician's
- o g) at the electric company
- o h) in a maternity clothes shop
- o i) in a veterinarian's waiting room
- o j) on a butcher's window
- o k) on the door of a computer store
- o l) outside a hotel

Task 2) *Underline the words with double meaning.*

1. A plumbing company: **Don't sleep with a <u>drip</u>, call your plumber!**

2. A sign in front of a snack factory: **Caution: Nuts crossing road.**

3. At a farm: **The farmer allows walkers to cross the field for free, but the bull charges.**

4. In a dry cleaner's: **Drop your pants here.**

5. In a New York drugstore: **We dispense with accuracy.**

6. In a pizza shop: **7 days without pizza makes one weak.**

7. In a snack bar: **Women are not served here. You have to bring your own.**

8. In an electrical goods store: **Don't kill your wife. Let our machine do the dirty work.**

9. In the office of an exterminating company: **We kill bugs dead, walk-ins welcome.**

10. Sign in a bookstore: **We treat you write.**

11. Sign in a real estate office: **Lots for little.**

12. Sign in a shoe store: **Come in and have a fit.**

13. On a taxidermist's window: **We really know our stuff.**

14. In a dry cleaning store: **Thirty-eight years on the same spot.**

15. On the door of a music library: **Bach in a min-u-et.**

© Ernst Klett Sprachen GmbH, Stuttgart 2011
Photocopiable
ISBN 978-3-12-534645-1

English Signs II

Task 1) *Explain why these signs are amusing. Which do you like best?*

1. Sign on a front door: **Everyone on the premises is a vegetarian except the dog.**

2. In a shopping mall: **Ears pierced, while you wait.**

3. On a main road: **Take notice: when this sign is under water, this road is impassable.**

4. On a shopping mall marquee: **Archery Tournament - Ears pierced.**

5. On a ski lift: **No jumping from the lift. Survivors will be prosecuted.**

6. On a fence: Salesmen welcome: **Dog food is expensive.**

7. In front of a car wash: **If you can't read this, it's time to wash your car.**

8. Sign at fast-food place: **Parking for drive-thru customers only!**

9. Sign over a restroom in a restaurant: **Used beer department.**

10. On a maternity room door: **Push. Push. Push.**

11. On a Music Teacher's door: **Out Chopin.**

12. Sign in a restaurant window: **T-bone steak $1** *(Then, in fine print underneath:)* **With meat $12**

13. Sign at a farm: **Trespassers beware! I shoot every tenth trespasser. The ninth one just left.**

14. Seen in a health food store: **Shoplifters will be beaten over the head with an organic carrot.**

Task 2) *What is wrong with these signs? Which of the mistakes were made on purpose to attract customers? Which do you think are the funniest mistakes?*

	yes	no
1. An ad on the subway in NYC: **Learn to read and speak English. Call us now.**	☐	☐
2. Australian phone box: **If you understand English, press 1. If you do not understand English, press 2.**	☐	☐
3. Hotel restaurant: **Restrooms to the left. Please wait for the hostess to seat you.**	☐	☐
4. In a dance hall: **Good clean dancing every night but Sunday.**	☐	☐
5. In a department store: **Bargain Basement Upstairs.**	☐	☐
6. In a laundromat: **Please remove all your clothes when the light goes out.**	☐	☐
7. In a maternity ward: **No children allowed.**	☐	☐
8. In a restaurant: **Customers who find our waitresses rude ought to see the manager.**	☐	☐
9. In a restaurant: **Open seven days a week and weekends.**	☐	☐
10. In a toilet: **Toilet out of order. Please use floor below.**	☐	☐
11. London hotel: **All fire extinguishers must be examined at least five days before any fire.**	☐	☐
12. Outside a country shop: **We buy junk and sell antiques.**	☐	☐
13. Outside a disco: **This is the most exclusive disco in town. Everyone welcome.**	☐	☐
14. Outside a farm: **Horse manure, pre-packed bags, $10. Or, do-it-yourself, $1.**	☐	☐
15. In a cemetery: **Persons are prohibited from picking flowers from any but their own graves.**	☐	☐

© Ernst Klett Sprachen GmbH, Stuttgart 2011
Photocopiable
ISBN 978-3-12-534645-1

International Tourism Signs I - Hotels

Task 1) *What is wrong with the following hotel signs? Correct them and write the correct sentences on a separate piece of paper.*

1. Because of the impropriety of entertaining guests of the opposite sex in the bedroom, it is suggested that the lobby be used for this purpose.

2. *If television set breaks, inform manager. Do not interfere with yourself.*

3. If you cannot reach a fire exit, close the door and expose yourself at the window.

4. **If you want just condition of warm in your room, please control yourself.**

5. In case of fire, please do your utmost to alarm the hall porter.

6. In the event of fire, open a window and announce your presence in a seemly manner.

7. Is forbidden to steal hotel towels please. If you are not person to do such thing is please not to read notis.

8. It is our intention to pleasure you every day.

9. Not to perambulate the corridors in the hours of repose in the boots of ascension.

10. **Please leave your values at the front desk.**

11. Take care of burglars.

12. *Visitors are expected to complain at the office between the hours of 9 and 11 a.m. daily.*

13. To call room service, please to open door and call Room Service. Please call quiet, people may sleep.

14. The lift is being fixed for the next day. During that time we regret that you will be unbearable.

Task 2) *What are the following hotel signs intended to mean? Rephrase on a separate piece of paper to make correct sentences.*

1. Depositing the room key in another person is prohibited.

2. **Fire! It is what we can be doing, we hope. No fear. Not ourselves. Say quickly to all people coming up down, everywhere, a prayer, always is a clerk. He is assured of safety by expert men who are in the bar for telephone for the fighters of the fire come out.**

3. Guests should announce the abandonment of theirs rooms before 12 o'clock, emptying the room at the latest until 14 o'clock, for the use of the room before 5 at the arrival or after the 16 o'clock at the departure, will be billed as one night more.

4. In order to prevent shoes from mislaying, please don't corridor them. The management cannot be held.

5. **Please hang yourself here.**

6. *Please to evacuate in hall especially which is accompanied by rude noises.*

7. The concierge immediately for informations. Please don't wait last minutes. Then it will be too late to arrange inconveniences.

8. **The flattening of underwear with pleasure is the job of the chambermaid. Turn to her straightaway.**

9. The passenger must get free the room before two o'clocks of the day they are abandoning in other case, as the passenger fracture the day and must the administration pay for full.

10. To move the lift, push button for wishing floor. If the lift should enter more persons, each one should press a number of wishing floor. Driving is then going alphabetically by national order.

© Ernst Klett Sprachen GmbH, Stuttgart 2011
Photocopiable
ISBN 978-3-12-534645-1

International Tourism Signs II - Restaurants and Shops

Task 1) *What do you think the following restaurant signs are supposed to mean? Make the necessary corrections on a separate piece of paper.*

1 After one visit we guarantee you will be regular.

2 *Girandole in the medium of the new thickets awaits you...salads, crunch-Mister, pizza pies. The sale to be carried enables you to be restored and to refresh you very continuously to discover the gardens.*

3 If you are satisfactory, tell your friends. If you are unsatisfactory, warn the waitress.

4 *Ladies are requested not to have children in the bar.*

5 Per hour of the lunch, you finely have the choice between the small one and the chart of season. – a sympathetic addressee pastoral for all the Family.

6 Salad a firm's own make; limpid red beet soup with cheesy dumplings in the form of a finger; roasted duck let loose; beef rashers beaten up in the country people's fashion.

7 Tacos and beautiful tarts are the order of the day.

8 *The manager has personally passed all the water served here.*

9 Topless waitresses – cover charge 15 dollars

10 Travelling potatoes, White whine Sardine in special roof tile.

Task 2) *In what kind of place, shop or building do you think the following signs were found?*

1 Bags to be used in case of sickness or to gather remains.

2 *Be careful of being eaten by small children.*

3 Customers giving orders will be promptly executed.

4 *Dresses for street walking.*

5 For your convenience, we recommend courageous, efficient self-service.

6 *Fur coats made for ladies from their own skin.*

7 Haircuts half price today. Only one per **customer.**

8 *Ladies, leave your clothes here and spend the afternoon having a good time.*

9 Please dial 7 to retrieve your auto from the garbage.

10 Take one of our horse-driven city tours. We guarantee no miscarriages.

11 Telephone instructions can be found on the backside.

12 **The Hall of Expectation**

13 To stop the drip, turn cock to right.

14 *Upon arrival at our destination, please wear your clothes.*

15 We take your bags and send them in all directions.

16 *You assist by composting yourself the ticket*

© Ernst Klett Sprachen GmbH, Stuttgart 2011
Photocopiable
ISBN 978-3-12-534645-1

St John's
Baptist Church

NO GOD – NO PEACE
KNOW GOD – KNOW PEACE

Church Signs I

Task 1) *Fill in the missing words to complete each sign.*

1. Come work for the Lord. The _____ is hard, the _____ are long and the _____

   is low. But the _____ are out of this world. *(hours / pay / retirement benefits / work)*

2. A lot of _____ will keep you in good _____. *(kneeling / standing)*

3. _____ to _____ before you _____. *(aspire / expire / inspire)*

4. _____ bibles lead to _____ lives. *(dirty / dusty)*

5. Forbidden _____ create many _____. *(fruits / jams)*

6. Give God what's _____, not what's _____! *(left / right)*

7. God promises a _____ landing, not a _____ passage. *(calm / safe)*

8. Give Satan _____ and he'll be _____. *(a ruler / an inch)*

Task 2) *Unjumble the words to make a church sign.*

1. _____
   (details – Free – heaven, – inside. – to – trip)

2. _____
   (church. – Do – for – hearse – not – take – the – to – to – wait – you)

3. _____
   (come – have – have – hear – one! – sermons, – sleeping? – trouble – We – You)

4. _____
   (eternity, – How – non-smoking? – or – smoking – spend – will – you)

5. _____
   (broken. – inside – Message – Sign – Sunday. – this)

6. _____
   (2,000 – for – management – over – same – Under – years.)

7. _____
   (access – fee. – God – means – no – Prayer – roaming – to – wireless – with)

8. _____
   (Bible. – daily – decay, – Fight – study – the – truth)

© Ernst Klett Sprachen GmbH, Stuttgart 2011
Photocopiable
ISBN 978-3-12-534645-1

Church Signs II

Task 1) *Read the following signs and underline the words which have double meanings.*

ST MICHAEL'S
ANGLICAN CHURCH
EXERCISE DAILY.
WALK WITH THE LORD!

① Are you wrinkled with burden?
Come on into Church for a faith lift!

② **Don't put a question mark
where God put a period.**

③ *God answers: "Knee Mail"!*

④ **God doesn't want shares of your life;
He wants controlling interest!**

⑤ GOD LOVES EVERYONE,
BUT PROBABLY PREFERS FRUITS OF THE SPIRIT
OVER RELIGIOUS NUTS!

⑥ **Having truth decay?
Brush up on your Bible!**

⑦ In the dark? Follow the Son.

⑧ *In the sentence of life
the Devil may be a comma,
but DO NOT let him be the PERIOD!*

⑨ WARNING:
EXPOSURE TO THE SON
MAY PREVENT BURNING!

⑩ **Wal-Mart isn't the only saving place!**

⑪ This Church is
"Prayer Conditioned".

⑫ **The best vitamin for a Christian is B1.**

⑬ **Worry is the darkroom
in which negatives are developed.**

⑭ IF YOU CAN'T SLEEP,
DON'T COUNT SHEEP.
TALK TO THE SHEPHERD!

⑮ *If God is your co-pilot - Swap seats!*

⑯ READ THE BIBLE...
IT WILL SCARE THE HELL OUT
OF YOU!

Task 2) *Express the meaning of the signs in your own words. Write on a separate sheet of paper.*

Task 3) *Which of the signs do you like best? Which signs do you think are most effective?*

© Ernst Klett Sprachen GmbH, Stuttgart 2011
Photocopiable
ISBN 978-3-12-534645-1

Klett

Warnings

Task 1) *On which of the products a) to j) do you think the following instructions and warnings were found?*

1. Do not drive a car or operate machinery after taking this medication.   o
2. Do not use for personal hygiene.   o
3. Does not enable wearer to fly.   o
4. Fits one head.   o
5. For best results, do not leave at the crime scene.   o
6. Remember, objects are actually behind you.   o
7. Not suitable for children under three.   o
8. Will only work when film is inside.   o
9. Do not turn upside down.   o
10. Not for children. May be used to construct words, phrases and sentences that may be deemed offensive.   o

o a) A birthday card for a two-year-old
o b) A camera
o c) On the bottom of a Tiramisu dessert
o d) A bicycle mirror
o e) A shower cap provided in hotel
o f) A superman outfit
o g) A toilet brush
o h) Alphabet blocks
o i) Children's cough medicine
o j) Gloves

Task 2) *Many warnings and instructions are given because of accidents that have happened in the past. Discuss what might have lead to the following warnings and instructions.*

1. Baby Oil: **Keep out of reach of children.**

2. Hair colouring: Do not use as an ice cream topping.

3. Portable stroller: Caution: Remove infant before folding for storage.

4. On a hairdryer: *Do not use while sleeping.*

5. On a muffin: Remove wrapper, open mouth, insert, eat.

6. American Airlines Peanuts: *Open packet, eat nuts.*

7. Beach Ball: ***CAUTION: It is not a life saving device.***

8. Bread Pudding: Product will be hot after heating.

9. Child's Scooter: This product moves when used.

10. Disposable razor: Do not use this product during an earthquake.

11. Lawnmower: When Motor Is Running – The Blade Is Turning.

12. Matches: Caution: Contents may catch fire.

13. Pepper Spray: *Caution: Never aim spray at your own eyes.*

14. Sleeping Pills: Warning, may cause drowsiness.

15. Microwave Oven: Do not use for drying pets.

16. On a cardboard windshield sun-shade: ***Warning: Do Not Drive With Sun Shield in Place.***

© Ernst Klett Sprachen GmbH, Stuttgart 2011
Photocopiable
ISBN 978-3-12-534645-1

Names, Shops and Professions I

Task 1) *The following people are quite famous in their field. Look at their names and match them with the descriptions.*

1. Alan Ball	o o	a) American football player
2. Anna Smashnova	o o	b) Neurologist
3. Tiger Woods	o o	c) Athlete
4. Cecil Fielder	o o	d) Tennis player
5. Chuck Long	o o	e) Baseball player
6. Lord Brain	o o	f) Gardener
7. Margaret Court	o o	g) Golfer
8. Margaret Spellings	o o	h) Government spokesperson
9. Pippa Greenwood	o o	i) Gardener
10. Larry Speakes	o o	j) Education Secretary
11. Chris Moneymaker	o o	k) Oarsman
12. Stephen Rowbotham	o o	l) Poker player
13. Usain Bolt	o o	m) Soccer player
14. Bob Flowerdew	o o	n) Tennis player

Task 2) *What profession or occupation should the following people have or not have?*

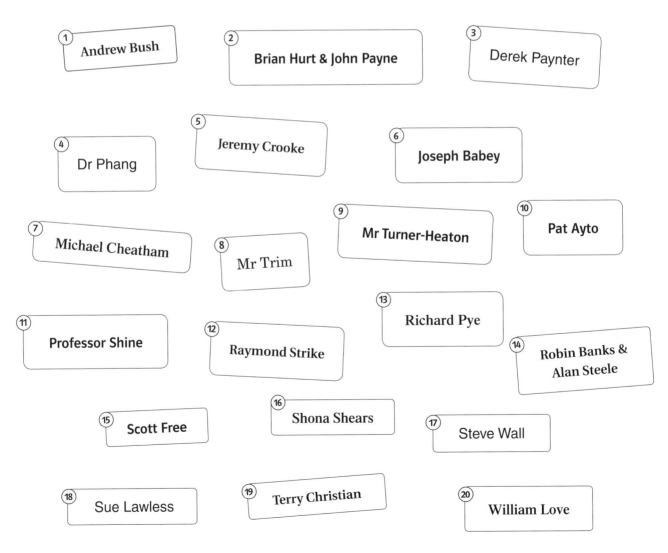

1. Andrew Bush

2. Brian Hurt & John Payne

3. Derek Paynter

4. Dr Phang

5. Jeremy Crooke

6. Joseph Babey

7. Michael Cheatham

8. Mr Trim

9. Mr Turner-Heaton

10. Pat Ayto

11. Professor Shine

12. Raymond Strike

13. Richard Pye

14. Robin Banks & Alan Steele

15. Scott Free

16. Shona Shears

17. Steve Wall

18. Sue Lawless

19. Terry Christian

20. William Love

© Ernst Klett Sprachen GmbH, Stuttgart 2011
Photocopiable
ISBN 978-3-12-534645-1

Klett

Names, Shops and Professions II

Task 1) Look at the following names of shops, restaurants and other businesses. What do you think they sell?

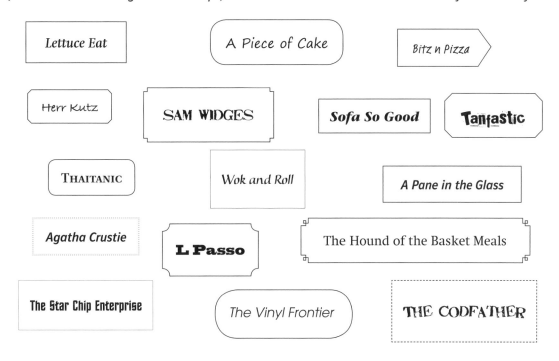

Lettuce Eat

A Piece of Cake

Bitz n Pizza

Herr Kutz

SAM WIDGES

Sofa So Good

Tanfastic

THAITANIC

Wok and Roll

A Pane in the Glass

Agatha Crustie

L Passo

The Hound of the Basket Meals

The Star Chip Enterprise

The Vinyl Frontier

THE CODFATHER

Task 2) The names are all puns and allusions. Can you guess the origins of the shop names?

Task 3) The following list contains the names of real places in Western Europe. Tick the ones you think are not in the United Kingdom.

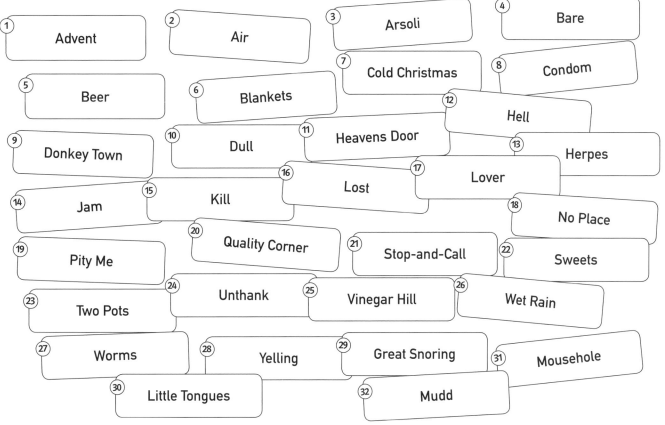

1 Advent
2 Air
3 Arsoli
4 Bare
5 Beer
6 Blankets
7 Cold Christmas
8 Condom
9 Donkey Town
10 Dull
11 Heavens Door
12 Hell
13 Herpes
14 Jam
15 Kill
16 Lost
17 Lover
18 No Place
19 Pity Me
20 Quality Corner
21 Stop-and-Call
22 Sweets
23 Two Pots
24 Unthank
25 Vinegar Hill
26 Wet Rain
27 Worms
28 Yelling
29 Great Snoring
30 Little Tongues
31 Mousehole
32 Mudd

Task 4) Which of the places would you like to live in and where would you on no account want to be?

© Ernst Klett Sprachen GmbH, Stuttgart 2011
Photocopiable
ISBN 978-3-12-534645-1

Miscellaneous

Anagrams

An anagram is a type of "word play", the result of letters being re-arranged to produce a word or phrase. There are many types of anagrams from the basic form of a random group of letters that can be re-sequenced to form a word or phrase all the way to a word or phrase, which when the letters are re-arranged produces another word or phrase. Sometimes it is possible to form a new word that has a similar meaning to the original, and there are other anagrams where the new word has the opposite meaning, sometimes called 'antigrams'. The copymaster activities use the latter two types.

Copymaster I: Task 1 is a matching exercise based on anagrams with the same or similar meanings, Task 2 uses antigrams. The learners should be allowed to use dictionaries if necessary.

Copymaster II: Task 1 works with famous people and the starting-out phrases give clues as to the person's identity. The first letters of the names have been given as a help. Task 2 combines anagrams and antigrams and the task is to draw a line between the original version and the new word. To finish off the topic of anagrams, Task 3 is a creative activity where the learners try to make anagrams of the names of people they know. This should be done in small groups of three to four learners.

Tongue Twisters

Tongue twisters are phrases designed to be difficult to articulate properly especially when repeated several times and at speed. Some tongue twisters produce results that are humorous (or humorously vulgar) when mispronounced, while others are simply intended to create amusement by causing embarrassment to the speaker.

The three tasks are examples of tongue twisters of different lengths. The shortest ones are in Task 1, where the task is not only to say them quickly but to repeat them as many times as possible without mistakes. This can be made into a competition. The examples in Tasks 2 and 3 are longer and it is usually sufficient to ask the learners to say them once only, especially those in Task 3.

In most cases it is probably better to do the three tasks on three different occasions, unless the degree of fun motivates the class to do them all on one day.

Heaven and Hell

The task is an interesting way to approach the general topic of prejudices. The first step is for the learners to individually match up the nationalities to complete the definitions of heaven and hell. Point out that they have the option of adding one other country in the space provided. They then compare definitions with their neighbour, then form groups of four, then eight and finally the whole class. At each step they compare and try to come to an agreement. Alternatively, the class can be divided into two groups: "Heaven" and "Hell", each group proceeding in the same way. When the class comes together to compare and comment on the results, a lively discussion can follow with prompts such as: "Why are there such differences of opinion?", "How can such prejudices be prevented?", "What do you think people from other countries say about our country?", etc.

The Thinnest Books in the World

Copymaster I: Task 1 is a matching activity where the students choose the people they think might have written the thinnest books listed. First make sure the class knows who the people are and then let them solve the task in groups. When reporting, the groups should also explain why that particular person was chosen.

In Task 2, the class themselves suggest who the author could possibly be. If help is needed, explain that thin books must be written by people who have no experience or are failures on the topic of that particular book. In some cases the people suggested will not necessarily be international but could be national figures or local people. Accept any person that the learners suggest if the reasons for their choice are valid. Task 3 is a matching activity but the learners can choose any country or nationality they wish. This can be done in groups who then compare results and discuss differences. The final task is a creative activity where the learners suggest other "Thinnest Books". 'If they need to be prompted, suggest one or two controversial people – local or national – and ask what books they might have written, or suggest one or two local, national or even international controversial topics and ask who knows so little about those topics that they might write a book on them.

Copymaster II: Task 1 is a completion activity where the learners have to suggest where, who or what the title might be. If necessary, prompt by taking the negative view, e.g. "What academic subjects offer few career opportunities?" Task 2 finishes off the topic of prejudices and thinnest books with a report about a UN survey. The task is to take words or phrases from the statement to fill the gaps. This can lead into a discussion about the degree of truth in prejudices that people have, how these originate and the problems connected with them.

Homophones

A homophone is a word that is pronounced in the same way as another word but with a different meaning. The words may be spelled the same way, such as *rose* (flower) and *rose* (past tense of "rise"), or differently, such as *carat, caret,* and *carrot,* or *to, two,* and *too.* They are the basis for many puns.

Copymaster: The task consists of a dialogue between a waiter and a customer which contains a large number of homophones that sound like geographical names. The task is to find as many of these geographical names as possible. Divide the class into small groups of two to three people. After doing the example in the text, let the groups try to find as many as they can. A large number of the names are well hidden in the text, so explain before the learners start to do the task that to get about ten of the hidden names would be a good result, fifteen would be excellent and over twenty brilliant! Check by going through the text asking the class: "Which name comes next?" Task 2 works on the same basis with a number of gaps to be filled with the place names in the box. Do the first example with the whole class together, then let small groups work out the rest of the sentences.

Refer to Page 6 for basic ways of working with the copymasters.

Limericks

A limerick is a well-known kind of humorous or nonsense poem, normally consisting of five lines. It has a strict rhyming scheme: the first, second and fifth lines rhyme, as do the third and fourth. It was made popular by Edward Lear in the 19th century. The copymasters offer a wide range of popular limericks with tasks based on various aspects of language.

Copymaster I: This task consists of eight limericks on which a gap-filling activity is based. The first letters of the missing words have been given as a help. Make sure that the learners know the rhyming pattern of limericks before asking the learners to solve the task in groups. After all the gaps have been filled, the class can recite the limericks either by individual learners or by groups in chorus.

Copymaster II: Task 1 offers limericks that play with abbreviations. The learners can work in groups, write down the full version of the limerick and then recite the finished product to the rest of the class. Task 2 is a similar word play based on words which are pronounced in a different way than suggested by their spelling. These can be dealt with in class in the same way as the previous task.

Copymaster III: Task 1 is based on tongue twister limericks which can also be used together with the previous tongue twister section. Let the groups recite the limericks as fast as they can, and the group that can manage the limerick correctly then chooses a limerick for one of the other groups, and so on. Task 2 is more reading for pleasure and shows a number of limericks that do not keep to the basic rules of the genre.

Language Learning

These tasks have language as their basis and are probably only suitable for post-intermediate learners. Although both copymasters offer more than one task, it is probably advisable – depending on the group – just to do one task at any one time.

Copymaster I: Task 1 is a gap-filling exercise based on linguistic terminology. If the learners are not familiar with any of the terms, they should be allowed to use a dictionary. Task 2 is a reading comprehension exercise based on a joke about language learning. Task 3 consists of a list of "language rules" that have been formulated in a way that already breaks the rule. The task is to re-formulate the rule in a way that keeps to the rule it is describing. Let each group work on four or five of the examples. The groups then read out the corrected rules.

Copymaster II: Task 1 is a matching exercise based on grammatical terminology. This is an activity that should only be given to groups that have a certain degree of cognitive knowledge of grammatical terminology. Task 2 concerns itself with the problems of English spelling. After reading the text the learners discuss the questions mentioned in the task and give their personal opinions on the English language. Although it is intended more as a fun activity, learners with a more serious approach to language might enjoy a class discussion.

Anagrams I

Task 1) *Find the anagrams in the box.*

1. a rope ends it   *desperation*

2. admirer   _____

3. best in prayer   _____

4. detect thieves   _____

5. enraged   _____

6. faces one at the end _____

7. has to pilfer   _____

8. lies – let's recount   _____

9. moon starer   _____

10. tender names   _____

11. the classroom   _____

12. voices rant on   _____

a sentence of death	~~desperation~~	presbyterian
angered	election results	schoolmaster
astronomer	endearments	shoplifter
conversation	married	the detectives

Task 2) *Match the following antigrams.*

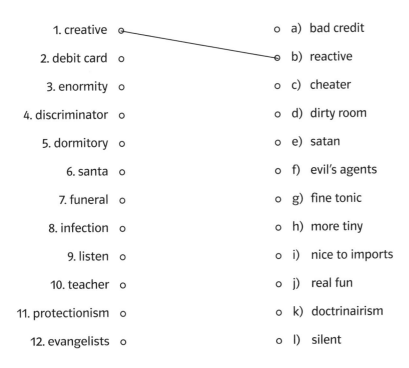

1. creative   o   o a) bad credit

2. debit card   o   o b) reactive

3. enormity   o   o c) cheater

4. discriminator   o   o d) dirty room

5. dormitory   o   o e) satan

6. santa   o   o f) evil's agents

7. funeral   o   o g) fine tonic

8. infection   o   o h) more tiny

9. listen   o   o i) nice to imports

10. teacher   o   o j) real fun

11. protectionism   o   o k) doctrinairism

12. evangelists   o   o l) silent

© Ernst Klett Sprachen GmbH, Stuttgart 2011
Photocopiable
ISBN 978-3-12-534645-1

Anagrams II

Task 1) *Famous people – Who are they?*

1. a bad man (no lies) – O*sama* bi*n* L*aden*

2. I am on a march – Ch_____ M_____

3. old west action – C_____ E_____

4. UN's said he's mad. – S_____ H_____

5. strongly psychotic, I'm funny – M_____

   P_____ F_____ C_____

6. that great charmer – M _____ Th_____

7. fine in torn jeans – Je_____ A_____

8. he bugs gore – G_____ B_____

9. I'll make a wise phrase – W_____ Sh_____

10. on any screen – S_____ C_____

11. Seen alive? Sorry, pal! – E_____ A_____ P_____

12. ten elite brains – A_____ E_____

Task 2) *Here you have mixed anagrams and antigrams; pair them up.*

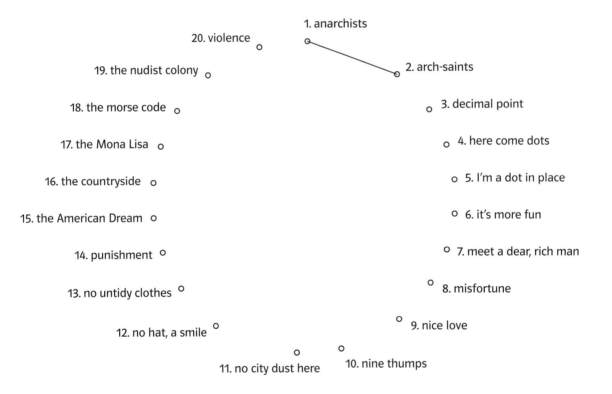

20. violence
19. the nudist colony
18. the morse code
17. the Mona Lisa
16. the countryside
15. the American Dream
14. punishment
13. no untidy clothes
12. no hat, a smile
11. no city dust here

1. anarchists
2. arch-saints
3. decimal point
4. here come dots
5. I'm a dot in place
6. it's more fun
7. meet a dear, rich man
8. misfortune
9. nice love
10. nine thumps

Task 3) *Can you make an anagram of your own name? Of your teacher's name? Of the name of a friend, your favourite singer, actor, etc.?*

© Ernst Klett Sprachen GmbH, Stuttgart 2011
Photocopiable
ISBN 978-3-12-534645-1

Tongue Twisters

Task 1) *Choose one or two of these phrases for your partner to say. Who can say the phrases fastest?*

1. Big whip
2. Freshly-fried flying fish
3. Good blood, bad blood
4. Red leather, yellow leather
5. Red lorry, yellow lorry
6. Six seals lick sick seals.
7. The epitome of femininity
8. Thin Thing
9. Unique New York
10. Wet rain

Task 2) *Choose one or two of these tongue twisters for another group to say together. Which group can say these sentences correctly? And which group can say them fastest?*

1. Does the wristwatch shop shut soon?
2. Many an anemone sees an enemy anemone.
3. Pretty Patty Piggy pickles plump pink peppers.
4. Randy wondered why Willie really wasn't well.
5. Round and round the rugged rock the ragged rascal ran.
6. Sam saw six shiny silver spoons.
7. Six slippery snails slid slowly seaward.
8. Stick a sticker where it's sticky where a sticker once was stuck.
9. The sixth sick sheikh's sixth sheep's sick.
10. Which wristwatches are Swiss wristwatches?

Task 3) *Choose one of these tongue twisters for another group to say. Have a competition. Who can read out these texts without a single mistake?*

1. Of all the felt I ever felt, I never felt a piece of felt which felt as fine as that felt felt, when first I felt that felt hat's felt.
2. Betty Botter bought a bit of butter. The butter Betty Botter bought was a bit bitter. And made her batter bitter. But a bit of better butter makes batter better. So Betty Botter bought a bit of better butter, making Betty Botter's bitter batter better.
3. Ed Nott was shot and Sam Shott was not. So it is better to be Shott than Nott. Some say Nott was not shot. But Shott says he shot Nott. Either the shot Shott shot at Nott was not shot, or Nott was shot. If the shot Shott shot shot Nott, Nott was shot. But if the shot Shott shot shot Shott, the shot was Shott, not Nott. However, the shot Shott shot shot not Shott - but Nott. So, Ed Nott was shot and that's hot! Is it not?
4. Peter Piper picked a peck of pickled peppers, A peck of pickled peppers Peter Piper picked. If Peter Piper picked a peck of pickled peppers, how many pickled peppers did Peter Piper pick?
5. She sells seashells by the seashore. The shells she sells are surely seashells. So if she sells shells on the seashore, I'm sure she sells seashore shells.
6. Silly Sally swiftly shooed seven silly sheep. The seven silly sheep Silly Sally shooed shilly-shallied south. These sheep shouldn't sleep in a shack, sheep should sleep in a shed.
7. Sister Suzie's sewing shirts for soldiers. Such skill at sewing shirts our shy young sister Suzie shows. Some soldiers send epistles, say they'd rather sleep in thistles than the saucy, soft short shirts for soldiers sister Suzie sews.
8. Theophilus Thistle, the successful thistle sifter, in sifting thousands of unsifted thistles, thrust thrice three thousand thistles through the thick of his thumb.

© Ernst Klett Sprachen GmbH, Stuttgart 2011
Photocopiable
ISBN 978-3-12-534645-1

Heaven and Hell

Task: *Fill in the following tables to describe your idea of "heaven" and "hell".*

Heaven is where the police are British, the chefs Italian, the mechanics German, the lovers French and it is all organized by the Swiss. Hell is where the police are German, the chefs British, the mechanics French, the lovers Swiss, and it is all organized by the Italians.

Heaven is where . . .

1. the beer brewers are from .... o	o a)	Belgium
2. the car mechanics are from ... o	o b)	Britain
3. the coffee is from ... o	o c)	China
4. the jokes are from... o	o d)	France
5. the cooks are from ... o	o e)	Germany
6. the financial advisors are from ... o	o f)	Italy
7. the footballers are from ... o	o g)	Poland
8. the lovers are from ... o	o h)	Russia
9. the managers are from ... o	o i)	Spain
10. the police are from ... o	o j)	Switzerland
11. the politicians are from ... o	o k)	the USA
12. the soldiers are from ... o	o l)	_____

(any other country you wish)

Hell is where . . .

1.   the beer brewers are from _____ .

2.   the car mechanics are from _____ .

3.   the coffee is from _____ .

4.   the jokes are from _____ .

5.   the cooks are from _____ .

6.   the financial advisors are from _____ .

7.   the footballers are from _____ .

8.   the lovers are from _____ .

9.   the managers are from _____ .

10. the police are from _____ .

11. the politicians are from _____ .

12. the soldiers are from _____ .

© Ernst Klett Sprachen GmbH, Stuttgart 2011
Photocopiable
ISBN 978-3-12-534645-1

ok Klett

The Thinnest Books in the World I

Task 1) *Who might have written the following books?*

1. "Guess Where I Am?" by ○	○ a) Amy Winehouse
2. "How to Be Good" by ○	○ b) Bill Clinton
3. "How to Find Osama Bin Laden" by ○	○ c) Bill Gates
4. "How to Lead A Team to World Cup Success" by ○	○ d) Donald Rumsfeld
5. "My Successful Presidency" by ○	○ e) Fidel Castro
6. "Programming without Mistakes" by ○	○ f) George W. Bush
7. "Stop Smoking Now!" by ○	○ g) Lothar Matthäus
8. "The Book of Virtue" by ○	○ h) Osama Bin Laden

Task 2) *Think of well-known persons who might have written the following "Thinnest Books"?*

1. "A Guide to Good Marriages" by _____

2. "What I would not do for Money" by _____

3. "My Life of Celibacy" by _____

4. "The Book of Careful Driving" by _____

5. "How to be Funny" by _____

6. "The Superiority of Women" by _____

7. "How I have Saved Taxpayers' Money" by _____

8. "The Gentleman's Book of Elegant Dressing" by _____

Task 3) *Finish the titles of the following "Thinnest Books" using words from the box.*

1. Teetotalism In _____

2. Enjoy Your Meal In _____

3. The (Comprehensive) Book of _____ Culture

4. The Complete Book of _____ Humour

5. _____ Ideas On Free-Market Economy

6. The Wit and Humour of _____ Politicians

7. Exciting Skiing Destinations in _____

8. _____ Hospitality

9. _____ War Heroes

10. The _____ Guide to Safe Driving

11. Safe Places to Travel in _____

12. _____

Australia(n)	America(n)	Russia(n)	Africa(n)	Italian/Italy
England/English	German(y)	Poland/Polish	France/French	any other country/ nationality

Task 4) *Can you suggest any more similar book titles?*

 © Ernst Klett Sprachen GmbH, Stuttgart 2011
Photocopiable
ISBN 978-3-12-534645-1

The Thinnest Books in the World II

Task 1) *Complete the titles of the following shortest books in the world. Compare with other groups.*

1. CAREER OPPORTUNITIES FOR _____

2. Everything _____ Know About Women

3. Everything Women Know About _____

4. FAST & EFFICIENT _____ PROGRAMS

5. _____ Logic

6. Men, _____ Creatures

7. Fun Things To Do In _____

8. Human Rights Progress in _____

9. Native Speakers of _____

10. Healthy _____ Food

11. THE ULTIMATE GUIDE TO CITIES WITHOUT A _____

12. Learn to Speak _____ in Five Easy Lessons

Task 2) *Fill in the correct words from the question asked in the survey.*

Some months ago, the United Nations organised a world-wide survey. Just one question was asked:
"Would you please give your honest opinion about solutions to the food shortage in the rest of the world?"
The survey was a huge failure because:

In Eastern Europe they didn't know the word "_____"(1). In Western Europe they didn't know the word "_____"(2). In Africa they didn't know the word "_____"(3). In China they didn't know the word "_____"(4). In the Middle East they didn't know the word "_____"(5). In South America they didn't know the word "_____"(6). In the US they didn't know the phrase "_____"(7).

And the Canadians put down the phone because they couldn't understand an Indian accent.

© Ernst Klett Sprachen GmbH, Stuttgart 2011
Photocopiable
ISBN 978-3-12-534645-1

Homophones

Task 1) *Look at the following dialogue in which a number of geographical names are hidden (cf. the example in the first sentence). Underline all the examples you can find. Compare with other people in your class.*

Waitress: "Why, mister, you must be <u>hungry</u>." *(= Hungary)*

Customer: "Yes, I am. And I can't remain here long, either. When is lunch going to be ready?"

Waitress: "I'll rush you a table. What are you gonna have? Do you want eggs?"

Customer: "You want to bet? I prefer turkey. Would you make the cook step on the gas a bit, please?"

Waitress: "Oh, that's a laugh! I'll ask her, but you'll hear her wails."

Customer: "Put a cube of sugar in my tea."

Waitress: "Don't be silly. Sweeten it yourself. I'm only here to serve you."

Customer: "Then mark my check, and call the boss for us. There's an error. I don't believe you know who I am."

Waitress: "I don't care a bean. You sure are a rat!"

Customer: "Some more of your jokes? What got into you? Do you think this helps business? Why be so chilly? Be nice!"

Waitress: "Don't give me that! Pay my cheque and don't you wait. I'll be seeing you!"

Customer: "I shan't be back, and I'll tell all my friends not to come here!"

Task 2) *Use the geographical names in the box to complete the following sentences.*

1. An early morning stroll along the beach will make me _____ cheery.

2. England not only has a blood bank for seriously ill patients. It als has a _____.

3. So many people want to visit the botanical gardens in London that you have to _____.

4. Two hitch-hikers who were on their way to Turkey stopped in Bulgaria and said: "_____, so good."

5. It is so hot in summer on the Greek island that British tourists just say: "_____."

6. A tourist was told to be careful in Chicago because some of the people in Chicago _____.

7. You have to be careful on top of the large tower in Paris, otherwise you might fall in _____.

8. From the top of the the large tower in Paris you can see all the sights. That's why it's called _____.

9. If _____ wore a _____, what did _____?

10. _____ or not _____, that is the question.

Brighton	Delaware	Eiffel	Kew	Mississippi	Seine
Corfu	Dubai (2x)	Illinois	Liverpool	New Jersey	Sofia

 Klett

© Ernst Klett Sprachen GmbH, Stuttgart 2011
Photocopiable
ISBN 978-3-12-534645-1

Limericks I

Task: *Fill in the gaps to complete the limericks.*

(1) There's a very mean man in Belsize,

Who thinks he's quite clever and w_____.

And what do you think?

He saves l_____ of i_____

By simply not dotting his _____!

(2) There was an Old Man with a beard,

Who said, 'It is just as I f_____!

Two owls and a h_____,

Four l _____and a w_____,

Have all built their n _____ in my beard!

(3) There was a young lady of Ayr

Who tried to steal out of church during

p_____.

But the s_____ of her shoes

So enlivened the p _____

That she sat down again in d _____.

(4) There was a pert lass from Madras

Who had a remarkable a_____.

Not rounded and p_____

As you probably think.

It was g_____, had long e_____ ,

and ate g_____.

(5) A glutton who came from the Rhine

Was asked at what hour he would dine.

He replied, 'At eleven,

At t_____, f_____ and

s_____,

At e_____, and a quarter to

n_____!'

(6) There was a young lady of Kent

Who said that she knew what it m_____

When men asked her to dine

Upon l_____and w_____.

She knew. Oh, she knew! But she w_____.

(7) There once was an old man of Esser,

Whose knowledge grew l_____ and l_____.

It then grew so s_____

He knew nothing at a_____

And now he's a college p_____.

(8) An elderly man called Keith

Mislaid his set of false t_____.

They'd been laid on a c_____,

He'd forgot they were t_____,

Sat down, and was bitten b_____.

© Ernst Klett Sprachen GmbH, Stuttgart 2011
Photocopiable
ISBN 978-3-12-534645-1

Klett

Limericks II

Task 1) *Read these limericks and write out the abbreviated words.*

(1) She frowned and called him Mr.
Because in sport he kr.
And so in spite
That very nite
This Mr. kr. sr.

(2) The sermon our Pastor Rt. Rev.
Began, may have had a rt. clev.,
But his talk, though consistent,
Kept the end so far distant
That we left, as we thought he mt. nev.

(3) A girl who weighed many an oz.
Used language I dare not pronoz.
For a fellow unkind
Pulled her chair out behind
Just to see (so he said) if she'd boz.

(4) There must be victims and victims without No.,
Who were slain by the deadly cuco.
It's quite a mistake
Of such food to partake
It results in a permanent slo.

(5) There's a girl out in Ann Arbor, Mich.,
To meet I would certainly not wich.
She'd gobble ice cream
Till with colic she'd scream,
Then order another big dich.

(6) The incredible Wizard of Oz
Retired from his business becoz
Due to up-to-date science,
To most of his clients,
He wasn't the Wizard he woz.

Task 2) *Read these limericks using the correct words.*

(1) There was a young curate of Salisbury
Whose manners were quite halisbury-scalisbury.
He would wander round Hampshire
Without any Pampshire,
Till the Vicar told him to walisbury.

(2) There was a young lady named Wemyss
Who, it semyss, was afflicted with dremyss.
She would wake in the night
And, in terrible fright,
Moved the bemyss of the house with her scremyss.

(3) A young Irish servant in Drogheda
Had a mistress who often annogheda,
Whereupon she would swear
In a language so rare
That thereafter nobody emplogheda.

(4) There was a maiden named Cholmondeley.
Who everyone said was quite colmondelay.
Yet the maid was so shy,
That when strangers were nigh
She always would stand around dolmondeley.

(5) There was a young lady from Woosester
Who ussessed to crow like a roosester.
She ussessed to climb
Seven trees at a time.
But her sister ussessed to boosester.

(6) There was an old man of the isles
Who suffered severely from pisles.
He couldn't sit down
Without a deep frown
So he had to row standing for misles.

© Ernst Klett Sprachen GmbH, Stuttgart 2011
Photocopiable
ISBN 978-3-12-534645-1

Limericks III

Task 1) *Read the following limericks as fast as you can. Then choose a limerick for another group in your class to read.*

(1) A certain young man named Bill Beebee
Was in love with a lady named Phoebe.
"But," said he, "I must see
What the clerical fee
Be before Phoebe be Phoebe B. Beebee."

(2) A tutor who tooted the flute
Tried to tutor two tooters to toot.
Said the two to the tutor,
"Is it harder to toot, or
To tutor two tooters to toot?"

(3) There was a young fellow named Tait,
Who dined with his girl at 8:08.
But I'd hate to relate
What that fellow named Tait
And his tête-à-tête ate at 8:08!

(4) A canner, exceedingly canny,
One morning remarked to his granny:
"A canner can can
Anything that he can,
But a canner can't can a can, can he?"

(5) There was a young lady of Crewe
Who wanted to catch the 2:02.
Said a porter 'Don't worry,
Or flurry or scurry,
It's a minute or 2 2 2:02.'

(6) The bottle of perfume that Willie sent
Was highly displeasing to Millicent.
Her thanks were so cold,
They quarrelled, I'm told,
Through that silly scent Willie sent Millicent.

Task 2) *Try and read out loud these unusual limericks.*

(1) There was a fat lady from Eye
Who felt she was likely to die.
But for fear that, once dead,
She would not be well-fed
She gulped down a pig, a cow, a sheep, nine buns, a seven-layer cake, four cups of coffee and a green apple pie.

(2) There was a young man of Japan
Whose limericks never would scan.
When they asked him, Why?
He said, with a sigh,
"It's because I always try to get as many words into the last line as I possibly can."

(3) A limerick fan from Australia
Regarded his work as a failure.
His verses were fine
Until the fourth line

(4) A young man from old Timbucktoo
Wrote limericks that stopped at line two.

© Ernst Klett Sprachen GmbH, Stuttgart 2011
Photocopiable
ISBN 978-3-12-534645-1

Language Learning I

What's another word for thesaurus?

Task 1) *Put the words in the box into the correct gaps.*

1. Why is the word _____ in the dictionary?

2. Why does the word _____ have five syllables?

3. Why doesn't _____ sound like what it is?

4. Why is it so hard to remember how to spell _____?

5. Why is the word _____ so long?

6. Why isn't there another word for _____?

7. Why isn't _____ spelled the same way backwards?

8. Why isn't _____ spelled the way it sounds?

abbreviation
dictionary
mnemonic
monosyllabic
onomatopoeia
palindrome
phonetic
synonym

Task 2) *Read the story and fill in the missing word.*

The Japanese eat very little fat and suffer fewer heart attacks than the British or Americans. On the other hand, the French eat a lot of fat and also suffer fewer heart attacks than the British or Americans. The Japanese drink very little red wine and suffer fewer heart attacks than the British or Americans. The Italians drink excessive amounts of red wine and also suffer fewer heart attacks than the British or Americans.

Conclusion: Eat and drink what you like. It's s_____ E_____ that kills you!

Task 3) *What is wrong with the following "language rules"? Try and formulate them in a different way.*

1. All generalizations are bad.
2. All grammar and spelling rules have exceptions (with a few exceptions).
3. And don't start a sentence with a conjunction.
4. Avoid jargon "buzz-words". Such integrated transitional scenarios complicate simplistic matters.
5. Btw, avoid the use of abbrevs., etc.
6. Contractions aren't always necessary and shouldn't be used to excess so don't.
7. Do avoid the use of the persuasive imperative – it does sound ingratiating.
8. Do not be redundant. Do not use more words than necessary. It's highly superfluous and can be excessive.
9. Don't use too many quotations. As Ralph Waldo Emerson said, "I hate quotations. Tell me what you know."
10. Everybody should use its possessive pronouns correctly.
11. Eliminate commas, that are, not necessary. Parenthetical words however, should be enclosed in commas.
12. Exaggeration is a billion times worse than understatement. So never, ever, ever do it.
13. I can't stand people who are sort of, you know, like, kind of, unable to articulate their communicative needs simply and clearly, as it were, so to speak!
14. In good writing, for good reasons, under normal circumstances, whenever you can, use prepositional phrases in limited numbers and with great caution.
15. It is wrong to ever split an infinitive.
16. As I said to the Prime Minister last week, name-dropping should be avoided.
17. Never use a big word when substituting with a diminutive one would suffice.
18. Never use a preposition to end a sentence with. That is something up with which I will not put!
19. Use the apostrophe in it's proper place and omit it when its not needed, and use it correctly with words' that show possession.
20. Who needs rhetorical questions? But what if there were no rhetorical questions?

 © Ernst Klett Sprachen GmbH, Stuttgart 2011
Photocopiable
ISBN 978-3-12-534645-1

Language Learning II

Task 1) *Fill in the gaps in the following Prayer for English learners by taking a suitable word from the box.*

1. May all my _articles_ remain definite and my _objects_ direct.

2. May all my _____ be answered in the affirmative.

3. May my _____ nouns remain in concord.

4. May my _____ never be irregular, weak or modified.

5. May my future not be _____ upon the form of my _____.

6. May my future one day be described in the _____ present.

7. May my _____ never shorten.

8. May my _____ verbs be regular.

9. May my _____ never be taxed.

10. May my _____ never be counted.

11. May my _____ remain active not _____.

12. May my _____ never be semi.

13. May my third person singular never be _____ or _____.

14. May my _____ past and my _____ present lead to a _____ _____ !

15. May my _____ never be fixed and my _____ never suffer, and may I never have a fixation

    about my _____.

affixes
~~articles~~
auxiliaries
collective
colon
conditional
demonstrative
endings
future
historic
imperfect
interrogatives
long forms
~~objects~~
passive
perfect
possessive
prefixes
simple
strong
suffixes
syn
uncountables
voice

Task 2) *Do you have problems spelling English words?*

The English Spelling Reform

In the first year "s" will be used instead of the soft "c". Sertainly, sivil servants will reseive this news with joy. Also, the hard "c" will be replased with "k". Not only will this klear up konfusion, but typewriters kan have one less letter. There will be growing publik enthusiasm in the sekond year, when the troublesome "ph" will be replased by "f". This will make words like "fotograf" twenty per sent shorter.

In the third year, publik akseptanse of the new spelling kan be expekted to reach the stage where more komplikated changes are possible. Governments will enkourage the removal of double leters, which have always ben a deterent to akurate speling. Also, al wil agre that the horible mes of silent "e"s in the languag is disgrasful, and they would go.

By the fourth year, peopl will be reseptiv to steps such as replasing "th" with "z", and "w" with "v".

During ze fifz year, ze unesesary "o" kan be dropd from vords kontaining "ou" and similar changes vud of kors be aplid to ozer kombinations of leters.

After zis fift yer, ve vil hav a reli sensibl riten styl. Zer vil be no mor trubl or difikultis and evrivon vil find it ezi tu understand ech ozer.

Ze drem vil finali kum tru.

© Ernst Klett Sprachen GmbH, Stuttgart 2011
Photocopiable
ISBN 978-3-12-534645-1

Definitions

Droodles (p 12)
Task 1
1. I can't understand
2. shot between the eyes
3. go overseas
4. small talk
5. maximum
6. turn right
7. go back
8. I forgot
9. to be or not to be

Task 2
1. mixed salad
2. first lady
3. Christmas *(no L – Noel)*
4. missing you *(missing U)*
5. water *(H to O – H 2 0)*
6. once upon a time
7. middle-aged
8. see to it
9. scrambled eggs
10. James Bond's Martini
11. born in the USA
12. higher education.

Task 3

Acronyms (p 13)
Task 1
1. After I return I'll never do it again.
2. Always late in take-off, always late in arrival.
3. Don't expect luggage to arrive.
4. Every landing always late.
5. Keeps losing money.
6. Lots of trouble
7. Prayers in (the) air!

8. Such a bad experience – never again!
9. Take another plane.
10. The worst airline

Task 2
1. Big money waste.
2. Funny Italian attempt (at) technology.
3. Fix or repair daily.
4. Had one, never did again.
5. Just enough essential parts.
6. Proof of spoiled rich children having everything.
7. The one you ought to avoid.
8. Virtually worthless.

Task 3
1. Double income no kids yet.
2. High earning worker.
3. Hard-up old person expecting full useful life.
4. Middle-aged urban professional.
5. Not in employment, education (or) training.
6. Single and desperate for a baby.
7. Single income no boyfriend and desperate.
8. Well-off older person.

Funny Definitions I (p 14)
Task 1
1f – 2j – 3c – 4a – 5g – 6b
7d – 8i – 9e – 10h – 11k

Task 2
1g – 2c – 3f – 4b – 5j – 6l
7d – 8e – 9k – 10h – 11i – 12a

Task 3
1. Tourist
2. Home
3. Airport
4. Christmas
5. Year

Funny Definitions II (p 15)
Task 1
1. father
2. relatives
3. bride
4. divorce
5. husband
6. birth
7. married couple
8. bachelor
9. friends

Task 2
1. passport
2. queen
3. ultimatum
4. peace
5. revolution
6. politician
7. vote
8. diplomacy
9. capital

Task 3
1. gourmet restaurant
2. adult
3. committee
4. alone
5. tomorrow
6. inflation
7. lecture
8. dictionary
9. psychologist
10. chickens

Proverbs and Idioms I (p 16)

Task 1

1. A bird in the hand is worth two in the bush.
2. A miss is as good as a mile.
3. Better to be safe than sorry.
4. Children should be seen and not heard.
5. Don't bite the hand that feeds you.
6. He who laughs last, laughs longest.
7. Laugh and the world laughs with you, cry and you cry alone.
8. Where there's smoke, there's fire.
9. You can't teach an old dog new tricks.
10. People who live in glass houses shouldn't throw stones.

Task 2

10a – 5b – 9c – 2d – 8e – 3f – 1g – 4h – 6i – 7j

Task 3

Original versions:

1. … is a penny gained.
2. … try, try, try again.
3. … it's worth doing right.
4. … iron is hot.
5. … than never to have loved at all.
6. … to forgive divine.
7. … a crowd.

Suggestions for funny versions:

1. … must be a mistake by the income tax people.
2. … re-define success.
3. … somebody has probably already done it.
4. … while the fly is near.
5. … than to have only lost.
6. … but to make a real mess you need a computer.
7. … the result.

Proverbs and Idioms II (p 17)

Task 1

1. A clear conscience is usually the sign of a bad memory.
2. If you must choose between two evils, pick the one you've never tried before.
3. It is easier to get forgiveness than permission.
4. If you look like your passport picture, you need the trip.
5. A conscience is what hurts when all your other parts feel good.
6. No husband has ever been shot while doing the dishes.
7. The best way to do the housework is to sweep the room with a glance.
8. Always yield to temptation, because it may not pass your way again.
9. There are no short cuts to any place worth going.
10. You cannot get to the top by sitting on your bottom.
11. Going to church doesn't make you any more holy than going to a garage makes you a mechanic.
12. A man who sinks into a woman's arms will soon find his arms in her sink.

Proverbs and Idioms III (p 18)

Task 1

1. Conscience
2. Interest on debts
3. too tired

4. host in a year
5. shepherd
6. guests
7. label
8. crocodiles
9. gets away
10. intents

Task 2

1. flies
2. soup
3. hell
4. prunes
5. chopstick
6. in touch
7. a monkey
8. shoes
9. bake bread
10. fishing-line

PC Language I (p 19)

Task 1

1n – 2e – 3m – 4h – 5k – 6a – 7b – 8f
9j – 10g – 11p – 12d – 13c – 14i – 15o – 16l

Task 2

1l – 2b – 3m – 4j – 5f – 6e – 7k – 8p
9g – 10d – 11c – 12a – 13h – 14o – 15n – 16i

PC Language II (p 20)

Task 1

1. grammar
2. to cheat
3. wrong word
4. examiner
5. CEF A1
6. a candidate
7. English
8. to pass
9. to fail

Task 2

Suggestions:

co-existed – mutual respect – in harmony with their surroundings –indigenous to their area – straw – sticks – dung, clay, and vines – peace – independence. – colonialist – ideologically – expansionist – culture – flesh-eating – colonialist aggressor – growth – progress –luxury – wealthy – indigenous – gambling casinos – gourmet steak restaurants – protest songs – United Nations – international support in their struggle for survival –fatty pork – Justice had prevailed – terrorised – free – social democrat – pigocracy – free schools, – free health care for all and cheap homes for all pigs.

Murphy's Law (p 21)

Task 1

1f – 2a – 3e – 4c – 5d – 6b – 7g
8j – 9l – 10h – 11n – 12k – 13m – 14i

Task 2)
1. Any
2. Anyone
3. Anything
4. As soon
5. Don't
6. He who
7. How long
8. If
9. Never
10. No matter
11. Nobody
12. Nothing
13. Only when
14. The sum of
15. What
16. When
17. Whenever
18. Where
19. Whichever
20. Whoever

OXYMORONS I (p 22)
Task 2
1b – 2c – 3i – 4f – 5j
6g – 7e – 8d – 9h – 10a

Task 3
1. Ethics
2. War
3. Works
4. Peace
5. Intelligence
6. Differences
7. Flight
8. Copy
9. Bush
10. Tolerance

Playing with Words

Tom Swiftly I (p 25)
Task 1
1h – 2e – 3b – 4j – 5i – 6c
7f – 8g – 9d – 10a – 11l – 12k

Task 2
1. fruitlessly
2. flatly
3. appreciatively
4. lackadaisically
5. disappointedly
6. acidly
7. delightedly
8. bitterly
9. weakly
10. pointedly
11. disarmingly
12. icily
13. hypocritically
14. disconcertingly
15. knowingly

Tom Swiftly II (p 26)
Task 1
1h – 2m – 3b – 4k – 5e – 6c – 7l – 8j
9f – 10n – 11p – 12a – 13i – 14d – 15g – 16o

Task 2
Suggestions:
1. "I've only got diamonds and spades."
2. "Happy Birthday!"
3. "I regularly read the weekly magazines."
4. "Have you got a table for four?"
5. "Enjoy the 4th of July party."
6. "I had to wait for hours at the doctor's this morning."
7. "Where's the back of the ship?"
8. "Call the fire brigade!"
9. "I have sinned."
10. "I've lost 10 kilograms in the last three weeks."
11. "I hate taking our pet for a walk in winter."
12. "I need some spices to stuff the Christmas turkey."

Tom Swiftly III (p 27)
Task 1
1. negatively
2. mechanically
3. mercifully
4. warily
5. wastefully
6. defensively
7. intently
8. overbearingly
9. privately
10. gingerly
11. reflectively
12. mistakenly

Task 2
1i – 2j – 3a – 4e – 5n – 6l – 7c – 8m
9h – 10b – 11g – 12o – 13k – 14d – 15f

They Never Die I (p 28)
Task 1
1m – 2b – 3h – 4f – 5k – 6n
7a – 8c – 9o – 10d – 11g – 12p
13j – 14l – 15e – 16i

Task 2
1. to another planet
2. off people
3. cold
4. to seed
5. off at a tangent
6. off-line
7. under
8. from bar to bar
9. to pieces
10. to a higher plain
11. down the drain
12. out of print

Task 3
Suggestions:
1. gymnasts / accountants
2. hotel receptionists
3. lawyers
4. astronauts
5. songwriters
6. photographers
7. train drivers
8. skiers
9. footballers
10. watch makers

They Never Die II (p 29)
Task 1
In all cases both answers are possible. My personal preferences are:
1b – 2a – 3b – 4b – 5b – 6b
7a – 8a – 9b – 10b – 11a – 12b

Task 2
1i – 2d – 3g – 4f – *(die = dye)*
5o – 6j – 7l – 8m – 9p – 10n *(thyme = time)*
11b – 12k – 13e – 14h – 15a – 16c

The End of the Road I – De and Dis (p 30)
Task 1
1d – 2e – 3f – 4h – 5b – 6a – 7c – 8g

Task 2
Suggestions:
1. jazz groups
2. bridge players
3. maths teachers
4. bankers
5. pigs
6. job applicants
7. brides
8. horses
9. teachers
10. misers
11. jockeys
12. pianists
13. waiters
14. examiners

Task 3
1. defrocked
2. delivered
3. delayed
4. devoted
5. delighted
6. decomposed
7. defeated
8. debited
9. disguised
10. dispelled
11. dispensed
12. diseased
13. disgusted
14. dismembered
15. disinterested
16. disappeared

The End of the Road II – De, Dis, Ex, Out and Un (p 31)
Task 1
1b – 2d – 3h – 4c – 5a – 6n – 7i – 8l
9k – 10e – 11o – 12g – 13f – 14j – 15m

Task 2
1. deflowered
2. disheartened
3. demoted
4. disconcerted
5. unleashed
6. expounded
7. outspoken
8. extended
9. disconnected
10. excelled
11. unmatched
12. outspread
13. outnumbered

Authors I (p 32)
Task 1
1f – 2c – 3i – 4j – 5h
6e – 7b – 8d – 9g – 10a

Task 2
1. Horace Kope
2. Beau N. Arrers
3. R. U. O'Kaye
4. Noah Lott
5. Dusty Rhodes
6. Mac Arronnie
7. Alec Trishun
8. Polly Tishens
9. Emma Fraide
10. Maggie Seins

Task 3
1. Warm
2. Naire
3. Mentary
4. Logge
5. Vator
6. Furniture
7. Beach
8. Vorce
9. Dente
10. Lynne
11. Orr-Nottaby
12. Bugge
13. Bulle
14. Nowe
15. Lies
16. Nasium

Authors II (p 33)
Task 1
1. Furter
2. Shaunerry
3. Birthday
4. Sudden
5. Shawe
6. Force
7. Cares
8. Punishment
9. Landyard
10. Power
11. Peace
12. Thyme
13. Law
14. Hyde
15. Fresco
16. Jobbe

Task 2
1. Holidays in the UK
2. How to Mix Cocktails
3. Join the Navy
4. Powerful Leaders
5. The Good U.S. Breakfast
6. A Bank Robbery
7. Horrible Neighbours
8. Hard Work
9. Unknown Destination
10. How to Stop Smoking
11. The Music of Handel
12. Where are you?
13. Art in the Middle Ages
14. The Big Wave
15. Too Much Ice-Cream

Classic Native-Speaker Mistakes

Spoonerisms I (p 36)
Task 1
1. A crushing blow
2. I must send the mail.
3. You've wasted two terms.
4. It falls through the cracks.
5. Lighting a fire.
6. Blow your nose.
7. Go and take a shower.
8. You have very bad manners.
9. A pack of lies.
10. It's pouring with rain.

Task 2
1. flat battery
2. wedding bells
3. flipping the channel on TV
4. bye all
5. right in your face
6. butterfly
7. I'm out of the shower.
8. speed of light
9. toe nails
10. steady as a rock
11. bowl of salad
12. save the whales

Task 3
1. Florida Keys
2. Santa Fe
3. Wisconsin
4. Berlin Wall
5. Carlisle
6. Castle Howard
7. Cornwall
8. Denmark
9. East London
10. Gibraltar

Spoonerisms II (p 37)
Task 1
There lived in a certain village a little country girl, the prettiest girl that was ever seen. Her mother was excessively fond of her; and her grandmother doted on her still more. This good woman had made for her a little red riding-hood; so everybody called her Little Red Riding-Hood. On the way her mother, having made some custards, said to her: "Go, my dear, and see how your grandmamma is, for I hear she has been very ill; carry her this little custard, and this little pot of butter." Little Red Riding-Hood set out immediately for her grandmother's house, who lived in another village. As she was going through the wood, she met a large wolf, who asked where she was going. The poor child replied: "I am going to see my grandmamma and carry her a custard and a little pot of butter." "Does she live a long way away?" said the wolf. "Oh, yes," replied Little Red Riding-Hood, "it is beyond that hill you see there, it's the first house in the village." The wolf began to run as fast as he could, taking the shortest way, and the little girl walked slowly, gathering nuts, running after butterflies, and making bouquets of little flowers. The Wolf got to the old woman's house first and knocked at the door--tap, tap. "Who's there?" "Your grandchild," replied the Wolf, speaking in Little Red Riding-Hood's voice; "I've brought you a custard and a little pot of butter from my mamma." The grandmother cried out: "Just push the door and come in." The Wolf opened the door, and then fell upon the good woman and ate her up in a moment. He then shut the door and went into the grandmother's bed.

Task 2
Tum sime afterward Hittle Rid Redding-Lood docked at the noor. "Tho's where?" Hittle Rid Redding-Lood heard the vig woice of the volf, and believing her mandgrother had cot a gold, answered: " Mit's ee, Hittle Rid Redding-Lood, who has caught you a brustard and a little but of potter from mama." She dopened the oar and hent into the wouse. The wig bolf, himming hidself under the cled-bothes said: "Cut the pustard and the little bot of stutter upon the pool." Hittle Rid Redding-Lood bent to the wed, and gred to her mandsuther: "Mandgramma, what ate grarms you have got!" "All the hetter to bug you, dy mear." "Mandgramma,, what ate grears you have got!" "All the hetter to beer you, chy mild." "Mandgramma, what ate greyes you have got!" "All the setter to bee you, chy mild." "Mandgramma, what tate greeth you have got!" "All the etter to beat you. "And, waying these surds, the wocked wilf fell upon Hittle Rid Redding-Lood, and upped her all eight.

Malapropisms I (p 38)
Task 1
1e – 2d – 3b – 4a – 5c

Task 2
1. (re)solve
2. proposition
3. eligible
4. influence
5. desisted
6. comprehend

Task 3
Nearly all need to be re-written, but these are suggestions for simple corrections:
1. … he or she …
2. Are our children …
3. … neither do we know about theirs.
4. … to do something to prevent it.
5. … for myself
6. … will be caught an prosecuted.
7. … help prevent there being a crisis.
8. … snatched victory…
9. … were the same group of people who …
10. …health care is not as good as it could …

Malapropisms II (p 39)
Task 1
1i – 2d – 3h – 4b – 5f – 6c
7k – 8a – 9e – 10g – 11j – 12l

Task 2
1. I have no idea where Osama Bin Laden is.
2. I have no idea what is going to happen.
3. I don't know everything that is happening.
4. I cannot prove everything I say.
5. I don't always tell the truth.
6. I cannot remember what I said.
7. I am not interested in what the President says, but he's the boss.
8. Our army is not good enough.
9. We do not know if he is still alive.

Howlers (p 40)
Task 1
1. orang-utans
2. abandoned
3. Highness
4. comma / punctuation
5. maggot
6. cemetery
7. turban
8. adulthood
9. origin
10. rabies
11. edible
12. distinguished
13. momento
14. monogamy
15. scapegoats
16. diseased
17. an imaginary
18. spinet
19. incontinent
20. martial

Task 2 and Task 3
These can be self-corrected by reference to a dictionary.

Letters I (p 41)
Task 1
1. corresponded
2. arrears
3. upper teeth, bottom teeth,
4. in connection with

Letters II (p 42)

Task 2

1. bumped
2. caused
3. fault
4. ran over
5. slow down / stationary
6. struck
7. backed into / vehicle
8. pavement
9. collided
10. swerve / hit
11. accident
12. intersection

Graffiti and Street Culture

Who Rules I (p 45)

Task 1

1f – 2c – 3b – 4a – 5e – 6d

Task 2

1. Horses
2. Stutterers
3. Homosexuals
4. Queen Elizabeth
5. The King of Siam
6. Matadors
7. Pessimism
8. Absolute zero
9. Synonyms
10. Apathy

Who Rules II (p 46)

Task 1

1e – 2g – 3d – 4a – 5b – 6h – 7c – 8f

Task 2

1. or luke?
2. no rules, ok?
3. OK or not OK? That is the question.
4. ko?
5. 00K?
6. OK? OK?
7. KO?
8. dominates, regulates, rules, ok, all right, that's fine

Task 3

1. Morse code
2. Irish dramatists
3. Spaniards
4. Examples
5. Personal hygiene (BO = Body Odour)
6. Flattery
7. Jargon
8. Hungarian wine

I used to be (p 47)

Task 1

1a – 2j – 3d – 4c – 5i
6f – 7h – 8e – 9g – 10b

Task 2

Something like:

1. … but now I constantly change my mind.
2. … but now I'm far too important to be left out.
3. … but now I would like to know everything.
4. … but now I annoy everybody.

5. … but now I just don't think about the possible consequences of my actions.
6. … but now I just think about my own thoughts and feelings.
7. … but now I believe everything other people tell me.
8. … but now I find it difficult to communicate my feelings.
9. … but now I always prefer to have the things I want.
10. … but now I rarely tell the truth.

One-Liners I (p 48)

Task 1

1o – 2n – 3f – 4g – 5d – 6c – 7m – 8j
9a – 10e – 11h – 12b – 13k – 14l – 15i

Task 2

1. As I said before I never repeat myself.
2. Everyone has a photographic memory, some just don't have film.
3. He got lost in thought and it was unfamiliar territory.
4. I have had amnesia once maybe twice.
5. Marriage is not a word, it's a sentence.
6. There are three kinds of people: those who can count and those who can't.
7. Time is a great healer but a terrible beautician.
8. Welcome to Utah and set your watch back twenty years.

One-Liners II (p 49)

Task 1

1a – A clear conscience is usually the sign of a bad memory.
2i – Always go to other people's funerals or they won't go to yours.
3c – As long as I can remember I've had amnesia.
4h – Be nice to your kids because they'll choose your nursing home.
5b – Change is inevitable except from a vending machine.
6f – Hard work never killed anyone but why chance it.
7g – I don't have the solution, but I do find the problem interesting.
8d – They told me I was gullible and I believed them.
9e – We are born wet hungry and naked and then things get worse.

Task 2

1. Monogamy
2. Telepaths
3. gambling
4. apathy
5. ambidextrous
6. impossible
7. tree
8. Vacation
9. Clairvoyants
10. anonymous
11. pessimist
12. mathematics
13. won't
14. bachelors
15. fat

Rhyming Slang (p 50)
Task 1

1. hair	a) belly
2. shirt	b) hand
3. trousers	c) legs
4. pocket	d) teeth
5. hat	e) nose
6. suit	f) head
	g) eyes
	h) mouth
	i) feet
	j) bum

Task 2

1. tea	7. gin
2. deaf	8. own
3. believe	9. stink
4. car	10. word
5. look	11. lies
6. pub	12. talk

Bingo (p 51)
Task 1

1 – 50	8 – 64
2 – 66	9 – 69
3 – 10	10 – 90
4 – 1	11 – 88
5 – 18	12 – 22
6 – 11	13 – 14
7 – 65	14 – 52

Task 2

1 – 23	12 – 89
2 – 37	13 – 8
3 – 57	14 – 2
4 – 20	15 – 3
5 – 6	16 – 15
6 – 9	17 – 84
7 – 82	18 – 77
8 – 19	19 – 16
9 – 26	20 – 70
10 – 45	21 – 33
11 – 7	22 – 13

Newspapers and Newsletters

Headlines I (p 54)
Task 1
1. HIT (affected)
2. BATTERED (beaten)
3. ACT (take action)
4. OF (for)
5. MAKE
6. SAFE (a safe)
7. LIES (remains)
8. AXED (dismissed)
9. DRIVE-IN / Board
10. BY (near)

Headlines II (p 55)
1. DEATH (fellow-miner dies)
2. TIME (prison sentence)
3. ARMS (weapons)
4. JOINS (returns to)
5. WROTE (performed) ON MONDAY EVENING
6. MISTAKEN FOR RABBIT
7. ON WATER in houseboats
8. RULE (give ruling)
9. CONTAIN (limit spread of)
10. BY (a road) ACCIDENT
11. 18 YEARS IN CHECK-OUT COUNTER
12. CRASH (intensive)

Short News Reports I (p 56)
1. bodies
2. normal service
3. cost of living
4. chair/platform
5. fired over rioters' heads
6. dress rehearsal
7. confirmed
8. no reason now why any of these things should be necessary now
9. the blind
10. responsible
11. Chamber … Potts
12. Miss Miller's rear end

Short News Reports II (p 57)
1. a day
2. This had to be removed
3. ended up in the maternity ward
4. claim some little part in the development of the district
5. gradually
6. replaced
7. without their clothing on
8. reduced them to nine
9. new Chamber
10. (fruity, well-rounded), (fine colour and full-bodied) (slightly acid, but should improve if laid down)
11. in large letters, so that those men who could not read might have the letters read to them
12. the option of moving the ball half a club's length away – or moving the crocodile
13. without any need to spend a penny
14. a chip on his shoulder

Church News I (p 58)
1. some older ones
2. by request
3. So ends a friendship
4. along with the deceased person you want remembered
5. sick of our church and community
6. the piano, which as usual fell upon her
7. baptized on the table in the foyer
8. Music will follow
9. A new loudspeaker … in honour of his wife
10. What is Hell … choir practice?

11. Get involved in drugs before your children do
12. to strip
13. to get rid of those things not worth keeping around the house. ... husbands
14. do something on the new carpet ... get a piece of paper
15. The Gates of Heaven. ... Please use other entrance
16. The sermon CONTEMPORARY ISSUES #3 "EUTHANASIA" ... TAKE MY LIFE

Small Ads I (p 60)
1. reference: waitress-served in appetizing forms
2. Hussy *(Husky)*
3. Live in
4. in convenience
5. undetermined
6. reference: in beautiful condition from grandmother
7. fowl / poultry
8. reference: antique desk with thick legs and large drawers suitable for lady
9. reference: Mixing bowl set designed with round bottom for efficient beating to please a cook.
10. heated
11. ants
12. pleasant

Small Ads II (p 61)
1. hard-to-find *(hard to please)*
2. Children *(Children's Meal)*
3. figure *(price/amount)*
4. neutered
5. dynamite ... travel.
6. do it *(treat them)*
7. eats ... fond of children.
8. Illiterate – Write today
9. 101 years old .. antique lover.
10. honest – Will take anything.
11. Our bikinis ... simply the tops.
12. tongue ... speak
13. Blouses – 50% off!
14. Semi-Annual – after-Christmas
15. Stock up ... Limit: one.
16. cleaning yourself – Let me do it *(do the cleaning for you)*
17. fresh ... produce
18. drink it all in *(drink in the scenery)*
19. your ears pierced ... an extra pair to take home (pair of earrings)
20. nothing else *(no other kind of stockings)*
21. beds, – other athletic facilities.
22. food – get hands dirty
23. tension in your home *(we come to your home)*
24. bottle with the big 7 on it and *(the letters)* u-p after.

Running Gags

RIDDLES I (p 65)
Task 1
1. go to sea
2. nose
3. hairy
4. laundry
5. reflects without speaking
6. going to itch
7. families
8. hair bug
9. steals from people
10. leaves its sheds
11. Hollander
12. brushes coats

Task 2
1l – 2i – 3h – 4j – 5c – 6k
7d – 8b – 9f – 10e – 11g – 12a

RIDDLES II (p 66)
Task 1
1f – 2e – 3d – 4g – 5a/b – 6a/b
7i – 8h – 9c – 10k – 11j – 12l

Task 2
1j – 2i – 3c – 4f – 5k – 6l – 7a – 8g
9b – 10e – 11d – 12h – 13n – 14o – 15m

RIDDLES III (p 67)
Task 1
1. Two in the front, two in the back and one in the glove compartment.
2. Elephones.
3. Time to get a new one.
4. An embarrassed elephant.
5. A jumbo jet.
6. An elephant in the fridge.
7. An L.A. Phant
8. Cinderelephant.
9. Elephants don't slip off your fork.
10. It was fed up of working for peanuts.

Task 2
1g – 2h – 3j – 4c – 5e
6i – 7d – 8a – 9b – 10f

WAITER, WAITER I (p 68)
Task 1
1. heat which
2. live
3. extra charge
4. breast stroke
5. day off
6. flea
7. swimmers
8. large
9. manager
10. laid

Task 2
1j – 2f – 3g – 4a – 5e
6d – 7i – 8b – 9h – 10c

WAITER, WAITER II (p 69)
Task 3

1 – v – b	7 – viii – f
2 – vii – l	8 – ii – g
3 – iv – a	9 – xi – e
4 – ix/x – d/h	10 – vi – k
5 – xii – j	11 – i – i
6 – ix/x – d/h	12 – iii – c

DOCTOR, DOCTOR I (p 70)

1. pen	7. liver
2. horses	8. invisible
3. glasses	9. dustbin
4. pencil	10. shoplifting
5. pack of cards	11. bug
6. roll of film	12. bell

DOCTOR, DOCTOR II (p 71)
Task 1

1. get home	6. Necks *(Next)*
2. true	7. Pull
3. turns	8. little patient
4. another room	9. notes
5. stir	10. last thing

Task 2

1. stealing	6. strawberry
2. liar	7. dog
3. glasses	8. invisible
4. schizophrenia	9. ignoring
5. second opinion	10. insomnia

Knock Knock (p 72)
Task 2

1. Wanda let me in? It's freezing out here.
2. Isabel broken, or what?
3. No, just me.
4. Tennis see.
5. Minnie? No not … - Minnehaha!
6. Mrs Zippy.
7. It's not Ida who, it's Idaho.
8. Toby or not to be!
9. Ella Man tree, my dear Watson.
10. Hugo first, I'm afraid.
11. Hannah partridge in a pear tree.
12. Police, let me in.

Task 3

1. I didn't know you could yodel.
2. … think of anything that's more fun than Knock, Knock jokes?
3. Who! Who! Who!
4. You got an owl in there?
5. … ong way to Tipperary …
6. … coming round the mountains when she comes.
7. Calm down, you idiot!
8. No, Cow go MOO!!
9. Bless you.
10. … awful headache after all these stupid Knock Knock jokes!
11. … more of these terrible Knock Knock jokes?
12. Not … Knock Knock joke?

Task 4

1. Sofa, so good.
2. Lettuce in please.
3. I didn't know you had a cuckoo clock.
4. Olive next door.
5. Hammond eggs.
6. Luke out of the window and you'll find out!
7. KLMNOPQRSTUVWXYZ.
8. Datsun old joke!
9. Tank you for opening the door.
10. I'm fine, Hawaii you?
11. Mary Christmas.
12. Four eggs-ample.

I say! I say! I say! (p 73)
Task 1

1. – iv. – h	5. – vi. – f
2. – iii. – d	6. – i. – g
3. – v. – c	7. – ii. – a
4. – vii – e	8. – viii. – b

Task 2

1. – iii – b	5. – vii. – g
2. – i. – d	6. – ii – a
3. – viii. – e	7. – vi. – c
4. – iv. – h	8. – v. – f

Signs and Instructions

English Signs I (p 77)
Task 1

1d – 2i – 3l – 4e – 5g – 6a
7c – 8k – 9j – 10h – 11b – 12f

Task 2

1. drip	9. walk-ins
2. nuts	10. write
3. charges	11. lots
4. drop	12. fit
5. dispense	13. stuff
6. weak	14. spot
7. served	15. Bach/minuet
8. kill	

English Signs II (p 78)
Task 1
Some of the signs are illogical (e.g. 2), some are indirect humour (e.g. 1), some play with words (e.g. 11) and some are just funny (e.g. 14).

Task 2
They are all illogical or ambiguous, and are probably all unintended.

International Tourism Signs I – Hotels (p 79)
Task 1 and 2
The fun of these tasks is primarily speculating on the meaning of these wrong sentences. There is no one correct version, many variations are possible.

International Tourism Signs II – Restaurants and Shops
 (p 80)
Task 1

The fun of this task is primarily speculating on the meaning of these wrong sentences. There is also more than one correct version, many variations are possible.

Task 2
1. airplane
2. toyshop
3. tailor's
4. ladies' clothes shop
5. supermarket
6. fur shop
7. hairdresser's
8. laundry
9. hotel
10. horse drawn sightseeing tours
11. phone
12. airport terminal building
13. washroom
14. airplane
15. airline ticket office
16. underground rail station

Church Signs I (p 81)
Task 1
1. work / hours / pay / retirement benefits
2. kneeling / standing
3. aspire / inspire / expire
4. dusty / dirty
5. fruits / jams
6. right / left
7. safe / calm
8. an inch / a ruler

Task 2
1. Free trip to heaven inside.
2. Do not wait for the hearse to take you to church.
3. You have trouble sleeping? We have sermons, come hear one!
4. How will you spend eternity, smoking or non-smoking?
5. Sign broken. Message inside this Sunday.
6. Under same management for over 2,000 years.
7. Prayer means wireless access to God with no roaming fee.
8. Fight truth decay, study the bible daily.

Church Signs II (p 82)
1. wrinkled / faith
2. question mark / period
3. knee
4. shares / controlling interest
5. fruits / nuts
6. truth / brush
7. dark / Son
8. sentence / comma / period
9. Exposure / Son / burning
10. Prayer
11. Saving
12. vitamin / B1

13. darkroom / negatives / developed
14. count sheep / Shepherd
15. co-pilot / Swap seats
16. scare the hell out of you

Warnings I (p 83)
Task 1
1i – 2g – 3f – 4e – 5j
6d – 7a – 8b – 9c – 10h

Task 2
The examples are strange because for most people the warning or instruction is unnecessary. They must have been given because of some accident or complaint in the past.

Names, Shops and Professions I (p 84)
Task 1
1m – 2 d/n – 3g – 4a – 5e – 6b – 7d/n
8j – 9f/i – 10h – 11l – 12k – 13c – 14 f/i
Task 2
1. gardener / tree surgeon
2. doctors
3. artist / decorator
4. dentist
5. criminal
6. children's doctor
7. lawyer
8. hairdresser
9. plumber
10. vegetable grower
11. french polisher
12. trade unionist
13. baker
14. bank robbers
15. defence lawyer
16. horticulturalist
17. builder
18. criminal
19. vicar
20. author of romantic novels

Names, Shops and Professions II (p 83)
Task 1
Lettuce Eat – salads
A Piece of Cake – cakes
Bitz n Pizza – Italian food
Herr Kutz – haircuts
SAM WIDGES – sandwiches
Sofa So Good – furniture
Tanfastic – suntan
Thaitanic – thai food
Wok and Roll – chinese food
A Pane in the Glass – mirrors
Agatha Crustie – bread
L Passo – driving courses
The Hound of the Basket Meals – snacks
The Star Chip Enterprise – fish and chips
The Vinyl Frontier – old LP records
The Codfather – fish and chips

Task 2

1. Lettuce Eat – Let us eat
2. A Piece of Cake – easy
3. Bitz n Pizza – Bits and pieces
4. Herr Kutz – Haircuts
5. SAM WIDGES – Sandwiches
6. Sofa So Good – So far, so good
7. Tanfastic – Fantastic
8. THAITANIC – Titanic
9. Wok and Roll – Rock'n Roll
10. A Pane in the Glass – A pain in the 'rear end'
11. Agatha Crustie – Agatha Christie
12. L Passo – Learners pass
13. The Hound of the Basket Meals – The Hound of the Baskervilles
14. The Star Chip Enterprise – The Starship Enterprise
15. The Vinyl Frontier – The final frontier
16. The Codfather – The Godfather

Task 3:

'Arsoli' is in Italy; 'Condom' is in France; 'Hell' is in Norway, 'Herpes' is in France, 'Kill' is in Ireland, 'Worms' is in Germany

Miscellaneous

Anagrams I (p 89)
Task 1

1. desperation
2. married
3. Presbyterian
4. the detectives
5. angered
6. a sentence of death
7. shoplifter
8. election results
9. astronomer
10. endearments
11. schoolmaster
12. conversation

Task 2

1b – 2a – 3h – 4k – 5d – 6e
7j – 8g – 9l – 10c – 11i – 12f

Anagrams II (p 90)
Task 1

1. Osama bin Laden
2. Chairman Mao
3. Clint Eastwood
4. Saddam Hussein
5. Monty Python's Flying Circus
6. Margaret Thatcher
7. Jennifer Aniston
8. George Bush
9. William Shakespeare
10. Sean Connery
11. Elvis Aaron Presley
12. Albert Einstein

Task 2

1 – 2	3 – 5	4 – 18	6 – 8	7 – 15
9 – 20	10 – 14	11 – 16	12 – 17	13 – 19

The Thinnest Books in the World I (p 93)
Task 1

1h – 2a – 3d – 4g – 5f – 6c – 7e – 8b

Task 2

There are no exact one-to-one solutions here, but basically anyone in the local national news, e.g. for 1. The British Royal Family.

Task 3

This can be left open to the group as with 'Heaven and Hell Task 2'. The examples are only intended to stimulate the learners' imagination.

The Thinnest Books in the World II (p 94)
Task 1

1. *(possibly)* PHILOSOPHY / SOCIOLOGY STUDENTS
2. Men
3. Men
4. MICROSOFT
5. Male *(or)* Female
6. Those Unknown
7. *(e.g.)* the Sahara *(or the local town)*
8. China *(or similar countries)*
9. Esperanto
10. Fast
11. MCDONALD'S / STARBUCKS
12. *(e.g.)* Hungarian

Task 2

honest (1) – shortage (2) – food (3) – opinion (4) – solution (5) – please (6) – rest of the world (7)

Homophones (p 95)
Task 1

- "Why, mister, you must be **hungry** *(Hungary)*."
- "Ye**s, I am** *(Siam)*. And I can't **remain here** *(Romania)* long, either. **When is** *(Venice)* lunch going to be ready?"
- "I'll **rush a** *(Russia)* table. What are you **gonna** have *(Ghana)*? Do you want **eggs** *(Aix)*?"
- "You want **to bet** *(Tibet)*? I prefer **turkey** *(Turkey)*. Woul**d you make the** *(Jamaica)* cook step on the **gas a** *(Gaza)* bit, please?"
- "**Oh, that's a** *(Odessa)* laugh! **I'll ask her** *(Alaska)*, but you'll hear her **wails** *(Wales)*."
- "Put a **cube o**f *(Cuba)* sugar in my tea."
- "Don't be **silly** *(Sicily)*. **Sweeten** *(Sweden)* it yourself. I'm only here to **serve you** *(Serbia)*."
- "**Then mark** *(Denmark)* my **check** *(Czech)*, and call the **boss for us** *(Bosp(h)orus)*. There's an **error** *(Eire)*. I don't **believe you** *(Bolivia)* know who I am."
- "I don't **care a bean** *(Caribbean)*. You sure **are a rat** *(Ararat)*!"
- "**Some more** *(Samoa)* of your jokes? What got **into you** *(India)*? Do you think this helps business? **Why** *(Hawaii)* do so **chilly** *(Chile)*? Be **nice** *(Nice)*!"

- "Don't **give** *(Kiev)* me that! Pay my cheque and don't **you wait** *(Kuwait)*. **I'll be seeing you** *(Abyssinia)*!"
- "I shan't be back, and I'll tell all my **friends** *(France)* not to come here!"

Task 2
1. Brighton *(bright and)*
2. Liverpool
3. Kew *(queue)*
4. Sofia
5. Corfu *(Cor! Phew!)*
6. Illinois *(will annoy)*
7. Seine
8. Eiffel *(eyeful)*
9. Mississippi / New Jersey / Delaware
10. Dubai / Dubai

Limericks I (p 96)
1. wise / lots / ink / iiiiii
2. feared / hen / larks / wren / nest
3. prayer / squeak / pews / despair
4. ass / pink / grey / ears / grass
5. dine / ten / five / seven / eight / nine
6. meant / lobster / wine / went
7. lesser / lesser / small / all / professor
8. teeth / chair / there / beneath

Language Learning I (p 99)
Task 1
1. dictionary
2. monosyllabic
3. onomatopoeia
4. mnemonic
5. abbreviation
6. synonym
7. palindrome
8. phonetic

Task 2
It's **speaking English** that kills you.

Language Learning II (p 100)
Task 1
1. articles / objects
2. interrogatives
3. collective
4. endings
5. conditional / auxiliaries
6. historic
7. long forms
8. strong
9. syn
10. uncountables
11. voice / passive
12. colon
13. possessive / demonstrative
14. imperfect / simple / future perfect
15. prefixes / suffixes / affixes